PROOF PAGE

Proof copy. Please do not distribute.

(Unless it's to someone really cool with, like, a million Instagram followers*.)

*Just kidding. People who follow Instagram celebrities don't read books.

PROOF PAGE

"No, no! The adventures first, the explanations take up so much time!"

- THE GRYPHON
Alice's Adventures in Wonderland, Lewis Carroll

0 (Introduction)

Dustin (from Nebraska) and Me

I live in the country but not on a farm.

This was the box my brothers and I marked in the pale green 4-H record books whose appearance announced the end of another steamy Kansas summer.

The designation seemed so perfect that I sometimes wondered if they'd added it just for us. We had no tractors, no feed lots, no fields to plow. My father worked for the state, not for himself.

And yet, we did have those two cows in the barnyard, and the twenty or so chickens next door, and the garden and the miniature orchard with the apricot tree we cheered on each spring, only to watch its blossoms lose their fight with a late freeze, year after year.

One fall day, after the record books had been turned in, I was wandering our non-farm when I came across a bright red balloon that was trapped in the fence near the apricot tree. I assumed the balloon had escaped from one of the plywood signs people sometimes nailed to trees next to our gravel roads to guide people to parties—eye-catchers alongside an arrow and a hastily scrawled *Turn Here!*

When I got closer to the fence line, I saw that this was no ordinary country balloon. This balloon had an envelope tied to it— an envelope that looked like someone had dragged it through our barnyard on the bottom of the boots my brothers and I wore when we fed the cows and chickens. Its corners were crumpled and its body was creased and it had stains that could very well have been poop-related.

Despite the envelope's unkempt appearance, I was intrigued. The balloon had clearly arrived from Somewhere Else— one of those places all those people were going on all those airplanes that crossed our section of the Kansas sky, leaving contrails that looked like a game of *Missile Command* frozen by the unreliable Atari my brothers and I had inherited from a family friend. I was fascinated by the contrails, wondering where those people were going, wondering if I'd have the guts to join them, wondering what contrails even were.

So, like a stranded sailor who's found a corked wine bottle washed up on his beach, I ripped open the stained envelope.

The letter inside was from a boy named Dustin who was about my age and who went to school in a small town in Nebraska—a comparatively far place best known for its football team, its corn, and how the first was named for the second.

At the behest of a wildly optimistic teacher, Dustin and his classmates had written letters to prospective pen pals before attaching those letters to balloons like the one I'd come upon, in the hopes that someone like me might write back.

I had questions.

How had Dustin's balloon made it all the way from where he lived in Nebraska to where I lived in Kansas? What were the odds that I would find it? Or, for that matter, that anyone would find it? His balloon could have landed in the field across the road, or in the top of one of the cottonwood trees that towered over our property. It could have gotten caught in a power line, or at the end of one of the satellite dishes that people in trailer parks invariably had, even though they lived in trailer parks.

Then again, none of that had happened. Dustin's letter had landed where I could find it. So I went inside and got out a pencil and a piece of paper and told Dustin I was fine and asked him how he was and explained my life to him. I probably used cursive because I had just learned cursive. It is likely that I told him about my two parents and two brothers and two dogs. I almost certainly mentioned baseball cards.

Dustin and I exchanged hand-written letters for a few months. Then, thanks to more immediate concerns, which for me included those baseball cards, the episodes of *He-Man* I watched with my brothers every day after school, and a longtime goal of getting a stick to float all the way down the drainage ditch that ran from the apricot tree to the barnyard, our correspondence fell apart, and my pen pal was lost to the fogs of the wider world, which I hoped, for Dustin, included growing up to be a "fierman."

For me, the fogs involved Little League baseball games and Boy Scout camping trips and middle school dances where I huddled in a corner, avoiding the scary girls huddled in the opposite corner. In high school, I learned about physics and chemistry and interrupted the path of a curve ball with my face, ending the baseball career that had seemed so promising back in Little League. I went to more dances, where I continued to huddle, avoiding the scary girls, who were now doing less huddling but might as well have been.

And then, after a blustery May day at the football field in my small town marked the end of childhood, it was time to follow the contrails. First, thanks to my grades, to Iowa for college. Then, thanks to my ability to put a ball through a hoop, to Greece and Spain and Russia and Atlanta and Chicago and Phoenix and Los Angeles. And Budapest and Buenos Aires and Basque Country, and now I'm just trying to impress you with my understanding of alliteration.

As I explored my versions of Somewhere Else, I didn't have much cause to think about Dustin. Or pen pals, generally. Until, that is, I overcame (some of) my fears vis-à-vis the scary girls, and started going on dates. Real dates, I mean—the kind that involved me picking someone up from her apartment and driving her to a restaurant, where we made jokes about the waiter and the bad bread, and after which we sometimes kissed.

It was after one of these dates—not one of the ones that involved kissing, probably—that I had a reason to think about Dustin and the bright red balloon.

Going on dates is always a hopeful enterprise. It is also usually a futile one. Dating, then, has a lot in common with trying to find a pen pal by attaching a letter to a balloon and sending it into the sky. It isn't just that dates rarely go as we think they should— that we can't control the way people respond to us any more than Dustin could control whether his balloon got caught in the top of a cottonwood tree or found its way into my eager hands.

It is also the nature of the dates themselves.

We tend to think dates are mostly call-and-response, ask-and-listen. Interviews, almost, during which we ask about the other person's day, or what movies he likes, or what she remembers of kindergarten. But in reality, the good parts of our dates are pretty one-sided. Once the date has gotten going, possibly thanks to the arrival of the wine, we listen to what the person across from us has to say, and then we say, "Aha! That makes me think of something!"

Maybe we don't use that exact manner of speaking, because doing so would make us sound like Doc from *Back to the Future*, but you see what I mean. We are inspired to take the reins of the conversation—to talk about ourselves, just like Dustin and I did in our letters. Of course, instead of being separated by the few hundred miles of airspace that were between Dustin's school in Nebraska and my parents' house in Kansas, our dates are separated from us by a bar, the arm of a chair, or a table's breadth. And, because we are adults, we have moved beyond sentence fragments that describe how one of our brothers keeps hogging the Atari.

Now, we tell stories. But these aren't just any stories. These are our favorite stories—stories we've told dozens of times before. We tell these stories because, in them, we come off a certain way: heroic or hilarious or broken but in a cool way, like the lead singer of a band.

We use these stories to explain ourselves, to figure out how we fit into the world, to decide how we feel about things.

And yes, occasionally, because we want to get laid.

This behavior could be viewed as duplicitous; it could be thought that we are manipulating our listener by presenting the best sides of ourselves. But come on. Telling our best stories: this is no more manipulative than wearing a flattering pair of jeans. And sometimes, it's downright essential. Maybe the person across from us has gotten a mistaken impression of us—that, because we made an offhand remark about wanting to learn guitar, we are the sort of person who would bring a guitar to a party. So we launch in: we tell a story that counteracts the guitar anecdote, maybe a story about how we once went to a party and there was a guy with a guitar and he was the worst person in the world.

We tell our stories to round out the listener's impression of us—to help the person understand that we are a whole human, with all kinds of viewpoints on politics and religion and love and death and our childhoods.

The stories in this book are *my* stories.

Sometimes they are the stories I tell when I am trying to explain where I came from. Sometimes they are the stories I tell when I am trying to explain where I'm going. Sometimes they are the stories I tell when I'm just trying to make someone laugh.

All of them are the stories I write on *my* wide-ruled paper, put in *my* envelopes, attach to *my* bright red balloons, and send into the sky, in the hopes that someone will find one of them.

And write back.

THE DATES

Kazan, Russia
Memphis, Tennessee
Phoenix, Arizona
Phoenix, Arizona
Los Angeles, California
Las Vegas, Nevada
Cameron, Missouri
Minneapolis, Minnesota
Barcelona, Spain
Kansas City, Missouri
Somewhere east of Denver, Colorado
Los Angeles, California
Los Angeles, California
Yosemite National Park

STORIES I TELL ON DATES

Paul Shirley

KAZAN, RUSSIA

A Sunday night

Unless you are a penguin or trying to catch one, central Russia isn't the place for nighttime walks in January. But taking nighttime walks in January: this is the sort of thing people do when they meet pretty Russian girls who also speak English.

This particular pretty Russian girl asks me if I know the story behind the reddish tower in front of us.

I look up at the tower in question, tilting my head.

"Well," I say. "Does it have to do with how it looks like a wedding cake?"

She looks at the tiered tower, then back at me, her bright blue eyes made all the brighter by her jet-black hair, a product of her Tatar ancestors. Kazan is the capital of the semi-autonomous republic of Tatarstan, I have learned.

"Not exactly. Although it is a romantic story. It has to do with the czar Ivan. When he conquers Kazan, he wants to take the city's princess as his bride. But she says the only way she will marry him is if he builds for her a magnificent tower. And he has to do it in a week. So the czar, he puts his men to work, and they finish the tower in six days."

"Impressive," I say.

I'm not being sarcastic. The Söyembikä Tower—as I will eventually learn it is called—*is* impressive, especially lit up as it is now, the lights below reflected by the bank of snow that runs to its base from the sidewalk we're standing on.

She nods, and goes on.

"The princess says to the czar she wants to see the view from the top before she agrees to anything. And then she walks up the stairs, looks out over the city, and jumps to her death, so she will not have to marry the czar."

"I see why they called him Ivan the Terrible."

"What do you mean?

"Well, if she'd rather be dead than marry him."

She laughs.

"Yes," she says. "But it is romantic, no?"

I tell her it is. Then I'm quiet, looking up into the clear night sky.

"What?" she asks.

"Nothing," I say. "It's just-"

I have trailed off because it has occurred to me that the tiers of the Söyembikä Tower also look like steps. And this has me

STORIES I TELL ON DATES

thinking about the process that has brought me to this frigid city on the Volga River.

She nudges me.

"You have gone from me."

"Sorry. It's just that sometimes it hits me, how far from home I am. I never thought I'd be able to come to a place like this."

"You mean Kazan?"

"Well, that. But also anywhere more than an hour away from my family."

She frowns.

"You play professional basketball. You must be good at going away from your family."

I can see her point. I'm only 26, but basketball has already taken me across a significant portion of the Western world. I've seen the Eiffel Tower, the Oracle at Delphi, the Grand Bazaar in Istanbul. I've thrown up in more countries (Spain, Greece, Macedonia) than most people from my hometown will ever visit.

Then there's how I look. As I stand here next to her, I'm six-feet-nine-inches tall. I weigh 230 pounds. I had the nerve to ask her out in front of half the restaurant where she works. I smuggled her into my hotel room in one of my oversized coats.

It must seem, to her, that it has always been this way.

1

Phoning Home

My mother looked at me in the rearview mirror.

"Go with Oliver Bledsoe," she said with a smile.

That's what my parents called my spiky-haired best friend. Never just "Oliver." Always "Oliver Bledsoe." I couldn't blame them; there *was* something rhythmic about his name. It felt like the slide on the elementary school playground: one dip and then another.

I got out of the car and raised a hand to wave away the dust our family's silver station wagon had kicked up when my mother had pulled into the gravel parking lot.

Rock Springs Ranch looked almost exactly like I'd imagined on the day the brochures for Science Camp had made the rounds in my fourth grade class. Behind the registration building were cabins with wooden porches and bunk beds I could see through their windows. A deserted swimming pool beckoned from the side of the building. Up on the hill: stables where the horses we'd ride on Thursday—the last day of camp—lived.

Oliver Bledsoe nodded at the building in front of us and we pushed through a screen door that slapped shut behind us. I poked my head over the counter in front of me, feeling a little like I did at the feed store while I waited for my dad to place an order on behalf of Molly the Cow and Beauregard the Rooster (and his hens).

"Shirley? Yep, gotchoo right here. Cabin 2," said some high school kid who was probably at least semi-stoned.

Oliver was assigned a different cabin, which was rotten luck. I consoled myself with the truths provided by my burgeoning understanding of the laws of probability. There were only four cabins and I still had two friends due to arrive—my allies in the inevitable battle with Stranger Danger. There was Darin Densmore, who scared me a little; he'd been diagnosed with ADHD, but he was smart enough to use it to his own advantage, sometimes making sugary snacks he called Hypercookies before school so he'd be particularly hard for our teachers to deal with. And Max Phalen, who had white-blonde hair and a laugh like a machine gun.

Surely one of them would be in my cabin.

Oliver said he'd see me later and marched off, displaying the same self-confidence I'd watched him deploy on the playground with a tetherball whipping toward his head.

Mom and I walked down the hill to Cabin 2, me with a sleeping bag under one arm and a backpack on my back, her carrying the duffle bag we'd so carefully packed. Inside, every pair of underwear had my last name on it.

We were earlier than most of my soon-to-be-bunkmates and Cabin 2 was empty. Rows of bunk beds waited inside another screen door. I couldn't help but think of prison, or Basic Training.

"Here," my mom said as she put down the duffle next to the empty bedframe. "Let's get your bed made now, so you don't have to do it in the dark later."

"That's a good idea!"

I said it with more enthusiasm than the situation warranted. My mother's words—"you," "dark," "later"—had delivered reality into my solar plexus like a dodge ball I hadn't seen coming until it was too late.

When my mom was finished, she appraised my sleeping area, declaring it shipshape with the tiniest of nods. Then she took a deep breath and said, "So, I think I'm going to hit the road, but you should stay here and finish getting your bunk ready, OK?"

She pulled me into a hug, told me she loved me, and pushed through the screen door. As soon as it slammed shut, the butterflies I'd been trying to quash became little stomach acid-breathing dragons. What had I been thinking? The closest I'd come to spending the night away from my parents' house was sleeping in the yard in a tent with my brothers.

I considered making a break for it. I'd put my hands on the station wagon's hood and the panicked look on my face would tell the whole story: we needed to go back to the cabin, get my stuff, and get me home. Maybe I could try my first night away from home next summer. I would probably be a whole lot more mature after fifth grade anyway.

I shook my head. I could do this. I just needed to concentrate on something small—wasn't that what Mom always said?

I opened the duffel and took out my travel-sized bottle of Pert Plus and the plastic soap dish I'd pillaged from the family camping supplies. I set them on the ledge behind my bed. Then I grabbed my towel, bright green, and hung it on the metal footboard.

I congratulated myself, pleased with the nest I was creating. I'd been right. Productivity calmed the little dragons.

Next up-

Hold on. What's this?

I pulled from my bag a Ziploc filled with bright red Hot Tamales. On it was a Post-it note.

"Love you," it read. There was a smiley face.

I halfway wished she'd left me a bag of locust pods and a note that said I was her least-favorite son.

I stared at the screen door. Could I catch her before she got out of the parking lot?

No! I had to do this! I was tired of being scared all the time. I wanted to be like Oliver Bledsoe, and Darin, and Max. Brave, unafraid, able to live without worrying so much—not about school, not about ground balls and their bad hops, not about the time I'd overhead my parents arguing about money. And definitely not about the worrying itself.

I allowed myself a handful of Hot Tamales. Then I put the candy away and looked down at my Timex. It served up the bad news like rotten fish: it had been six minutes since my mother had exited Screen Door Left. At this rate, I was going to fall apart by dinnertime.

I ran through the options.

Drown myself in the lake. Fake an illness. Wrap myself in my green towel and curl up under my bed like a caterpillar in its cocoon.

Wait! I had friends!

I put the duffel back together and slipped through the screen door which, by now, was starting to get more use as boys began to populate my cabin. I ignored (cursed) the jaunty way they piled in toward their bunks, telling myself I'd feel better when I got outside and found my compatriots.

And sure enough, when I tracked down Darin and Max near the administration building, the dragons reverted to something between themselves and butterflies. Angry pelicans, maybe. Especially because I had something Darin and Max didn't: information. I'd be able to help them figure out this Science Camp thing, play elder statesman based on the wealth of knowledge I'd banked.

I hovered nearby while Darin's dad helped my two friends check in before telling us to have fun and roaring off in the Densmore family's green Mercury.

As the parking lot dust settled, I licked my chops, ready to drop some knowledge.

Until Oliver Bledsoe showed up, confidence seeping from under his red Umbro shorts. He compared cabin assignments with Darin and Max and—damn you, probability!—not only were none of my friends in *my* cabin, all of my friends were in the same, *other* cabin.

Oliver told Darin and Max to "Come on!" and the three of them tore off down the hill, laughing and smiling and thrilled to be free. I stood in the parking lot, feeling like Wile E. Coyote when he realizes the cliff isn't there anymore.

I trudged back to my cabin, nowhere else to go. There I discovered that my bunkmate was a rich kid from Topeka—all blond hair and big teeth and one of those bright, short-sleeve shirts with the collars. We shook hands and went through the usual stuff: what school do you go to, do you play baseball, who's your favorite team.

I didn't get up the nerve to ask him if he missed his parents, because it was becoming clear that I was the only one who did.

At suppertime, our cabin leader marshaled us for the walk up to the main hall to eat. I would have given anything to be him. He was so confident, so sure of himself, so much older. I was willing to bet he didn't miss home.

The mess hall was another set of questions: where to pick up your tray, where to get your food, where to sit so you could push your food around the tray while missing your mother's goulash.

We were instructed to stay with our cabins at the tables assigned, and, once again, I was separated from my friends. Not that they seemed to mind. I saw Oliver and Darin and Max across the room, laughing and joshing with new friends they'd made.

I blinked away the tears that were sprouting at the corners of my eyes.

After supper, we walked to the camp's amphitheater where an official-looking fellow welcomed us to our week at Science Camp, saying all sorts of parental things that made me feel like someone would care if I lived or died. And then he said he had a surprise: all the way from Florida, someone from NASA!

Finally, some good news.

Like every other kid who grew up in the Eighties under the shadow of what seemed like bi-monthly flights of the Space Shuttle, I wanted to be an astronaut someday. This dream would eventually be compromised by several factors, not the least of which being my arrival at a height far too great for any space suit NASA has ever made. But the summer after fourth grade, I cared about three things:

1) Dinosaurs
2) Baseball
3) Space

The man from NASA told us he was some kind of test pilot, which was pretty close to an astronaut, you have to admit. Then he took a black brick from a box on a nearby table.

"Anybody know what this is?"

The group was too transfixed even for a smart-aleck remark.

"No?" he said. "Well, watch this."

From the same box, he took hold of a butane torch, lit it, and held the blue flame to the bottom of the brick. It shone red, just like-

"Kids, this block is one of those that sits on the bottom of the space shuttle, that helps protect it during re-entry."

We gasped as one. It was just like the animations we'd all seen in class, only in real life! He continued to hold the glowing brick as we marveled at whatever sorcery had allowed this to happen, and I fumbled for the disposable camera my mom had armed me with. I got it out just in time to snap the one picture I took at Science Camp—a man holding an orange brick and what looks like a caulking gun, all of it very blurry. I'd rushed the shot, not wanting anyone to notice what I was doing.

It was dark when the program was over. The camp leader told us we had an hour before lights out, but that we should head back to the cabins. He didn't want anyone wandering off into the woods because he didn't want to deal with our parents if one of us disappeared. It got a hearty laugh from everyone but me. At the mention of "parents," the dragons awoke.

On the walk back to my cabin, the man from NASA was long forgotten. Home was all I could think about. What if I couldn't sleep here? What if I had to get up and go to the latrine in the middle of the night? What if someone laughed at my pajamas, which had football players on them and which had come out of the business end of my mother's sewing machine?

I looked around as we slid as one through the darkness, hoping for a sign that someone else was feeling like I was. But no, everyone else looked thrilled by whatever adventures lay ahead, like the kids from the Peter Pan cartoon I'd watched not so long ago on *The Wonderful World of Disney*.

When I got to my bunk, I busied myself with the arrangement of my pillow and sleeping bag, trying to breathe, telling myself this would all be over soon.

BUT NOT SOON ENOUGH, my brain screamed. The seconds were passing as if in some kind of sludge; it was going to be years before the Thursday horse rides. Why had I agreed to this? Why had I left home? What had I been thinking?

Then it hit me: I had an option—a ripcord I could pull to keep from forming a Paul-sized crater on the ground that was speeding toward me.

I darted for the door, passing kids who were carrying their toothbrushes to and from the latrine building. I walked up the path toward the main building.

"Hey, kid! What are you doing?"

It was one of the high school-aged counselors, walking out of the main building.

"I, uh-"

I held out my neon-green Velcro wallet as if that would explain everything. I'd written instructions for how to call home on a tiny piece of notecard that was tucked neatly into the space reserved for driver's licenses.

When I realized that my explanation hadn't been close to sufficient, I said, "I'm looking for the phone."

"Oh."

His eyes held steady on mine as he decided what to do. He'd probably been briefed on the signs of homesickness, told that calls home on the first night weren't an indicator of stability. But then he shrugged.

"OK. You need a dime?"

I shook my head.

"Cool. Make sure you're in bed by ten, huh?"

He pointed behind him, to a door.

"Phone's in there."

I thanked him and hustled past. At the phone, I set the tiny piece of card stock on top of the phone's black iron molding and analyzed the beast in front of me. I'd never used a pay phone before. Country mouse and all that.

"Insert coins to place a call," the coin slot read. When my father had explained how to use the family's calling card, he'd said all I had to do was dial a 1-800 number, which was free.

Maybe I needed that dime after all. I looked at the door through which I'd just come. Then back at the phone.

No, I told myself. Dad said you didn't need any coins.

I picked up the receiver and dialed the number I'd scrawled on the note card while sitting at the same kitchen table my brothers and I occasionally turned into an inconveniently oblong Nerf ping-pong table.

I heard two rings, and then a voice.

"How can I direct your call?"

This was not how this was supposed to go. I was supposed to hear an *automated* voice, one that said, "Please enter your calling card number."

I did what any reasonable 10-year-old would do: I hung up. Then, my hand on the receiver, I stared at the phone box and took a deep breath before dialing again, this time more careful that I was getting the number right.

"How can I direct your call?"

I hung up again. Now I was breathing hard, sweating, nearing panic. I was so close to contact with my parents, my brothers, the basketball hoop attached above the door in their room. But maybe this riddle was too much for me.

Another deep breath and I dialed yet again.

"How can I direct your call?"

This time, I didn't hang up.

"Hi," I said, my voice sounding tinny and mouse-like, even to me. "I'm trying to call home with this calling card and-"

She interrupted me.

"You probably want to dial-"

And here she told me the number I already had, sending down my spine a shiver worthy of one of the *Friday the 13th* movies that were haunting the era's teenagers.

"I tried that," I said.

"Huh. Well, do you want to try a collect call?"

Collect call. Collect call. What's a collect call?

"Do you know what a collect call is?"

I shook my head. Then, recalling that the operator couldn't hear my brain rattling around, I said that I did not.

I could feel her smile over the line. I relaxed my grip on the receiver, noticing as I did that my knuckles were white.

"OK, well, you give me the number, and I'll place the call. When the other party answers, I'll ask if they'll accept the charges associated with the call. Assuming they say yes, you'll be connected."

This raised a couple of issues. One, I would be giving a stranger my home phone number? It seemed like I'd been warned against that. And two, I couldn't imagine "accept the charges" was a thing my dad liked hearing. But in my state, she could have asked for one of my testicles and I would have considered it. Especially because, at age 10, I didn't yet have much use for my testicles.

I hadn't said anything while running through the options in my head.

"That sound OK?"

"Yeah," I said.

She dialed the number. After three rings, I heard my mother pick up, surprise in her voice at the late call.

"I have a…Paul Shirley on the other end, making a collect call. Will you accept the charges?"

While the operator was at work, connecting my mother and me using whatever cables or tubes or wizardry was at her disposal, I'd begun rehearsing what I would say when my mother picked up. I would keep it light and bouncy. Nonchalant, that was the word. In fact, I was feeling pretty *nonchalant* already. After all, I was just a son calling home with the help of this nice operator lady. Pretty standard stuff, when you thought about it. I'd make the call. I'd go back to the cabin. I'd go to sleep.

What had I been so worried about?

But then my mom said, "Paul?"

And all she got in return was a whimper and the sound of her eldest son bursting into tears.

Eventually, after several entreaties for me to "just take a breath," my mother got me calmed down.

I asked her what was happening there, at home.

"Not much," she said. "Just getting everyone ready for bed. How's camp? I mean, did your friends get there?"

Yeah, mom, they came. But they're all so far away and I don't understand why someone didn't think of this—why they didn't put us in the same cabin, so it wouldn't be so scary.

"Yeah," I said. Then I took a breath and asked the question that had been on my mind, even if I hadn't really known it.

"Mom? Could you, uh…could you just come get me in the morning?"

I didn't expect her to say yes. Even if, as I reasoned, it wouldn't have been all that hard for her to save me from this misery—just an hour to me and an hour back.

But then I heard nothing from her end, and I realized: she was considering it!

By my mother's telling, decades later, that pause encompassed everything that is awful about parenting. She wanted to make my life easier; she wanted to drive there that night, pick me up, carry me home.

But she didn't. Instead, she gave me a few discrete goals: "Have ten Hot Tamales. Brush your teeth. Get into bed. Everything will look better in the morning."

Then she said, "Look, Paul, you're not missing anything here."

Easy for you to say, I thought.

I imagined the sorts of things my brothers and I might have been doing. Or, more accurately, what we might do the next day, as my brothers were probably asleep.

"Try to have fun. Keep yourself busy."

I wiped the tears and snot that had dribbled onto my shirt.

"OK," I said, cowed.

We said our I love yous and our goodnights, and I hung up, trying again to wipe my eyes. I walked back to my cabin, keeping my head down as best I could in case the counselor was still around.

I spent the next day in a fragile state. If someone had insulted my shirt or stepped on my foot in the lunch line, I would almost certainly have burst into tears. But that day passed, and so did the next few. My bag of Hot Tamales got smaller and the dragons got tamer. Pretty soon, it was Thursday morning and we were taking the horse rides we'd been promised. Then it was Thursday afternoon and Oliver Bledsoe's mom was pulling into the fan-shaped parking lot to pick us up. When she got there, I was in the middle of pretending I cared about building a kite the counselors had said we could take home with us.

When I got outside and explained the kite situation, Oliver's mom asked if I wanted to go back inside and finish it. I looked back at the low-slung building—the building where Oliver and I had peered over the counter, just four days before, asking about our cabin assignments.

And the building where, that same night, I'd made my call.

"No," I said. "They can keep it."

I jogged to my cabin, where I put my bright green towel back in my duffel bag. I dropped the empty Ziploc in a trashcan outside. I got into the Bledsoe family's station wagon. Oliver's mom set the air conditioning on max. And I had the hour-long car ride I'd wanted four nights before.

Science Camp was not my last dance with homesickness. I would suffer again the following summer, at Boy Scout Camp. And the next year, at Basketball Camp. I suffered even when I went off to college. The night after my father helped me construct a set of shelves in my dorm room, I lay awake in the hotel room my parents had rented for the night, next to my brother Tom, who was only seven, with one wish on my mind: that I could go home with him the next day.

But each of those steps led to the next one, like the tiers of the Söyembikä Tower, and eventually, I learned to make a home wherever I was: Atlanta. Barcelona. Chicago. The Denver Airport. The engineering department at Iowa State University.

Or Kazan, Russia.

"Oh, I see," says the Tatar girl. "You were almost like the princess."

"You mean the princess who jumped from the tower?"

She nods and I consider her analogy. Probably, one of my eyebrows is higher than the other. This is an expression I make when I am thinking about things.

"But," I say. "Wouldn't I be *exactly* like the princess? Because just like her, I jumped."

She sighs in the way Russians do. They are a grimmer people than we are, but they are also a people who are far better acquainted with allegory.

"No, you were not the princess. Because you didn't jump from the tower."

"But I did jump, into the unknown."

Frustrated, she shakes her head.

"No," she says. "Life is the unknown. Death is known, certain, predictable."

I look at her, twisting my head again, but not because anything about her is crooked. She is perfectly straight and, as it turns out, perfectly correct.

At Science Camp, I *tried* to be like the princess; I *tried* to take the easy way out—to jump away from an unknown future with Ivan the Terrible and toward the certainty provided by death.

But I didn't.

This didn't happen because I was particularly courageous or because I knew what was best for me or because I was going to force myself to endure the short-term misery of four nights of Science Camp in return for the long-term gain of the awareness that I could survive in unfamiliar environs.

It happened only because, unlike the princess, I was lucky. I had someone around to stop me: someone who held me close by keeping me at arm's length.

My mother, who loved me enough to set me free.

MEMPHIS

A Monday afternoon

"Excuse me," I say.

She looks up from the phone she's bent over, her elbows on her knees. There isn't a green light in her brown eyes, but there isn't a red one, either.

I take a sip of air, like I'm about to shoot a free throw.

"This might be a little forward," I say. "But I saw you back in the Kansas City airport and now you're here, like me. So I thought I'd come say hi."

"You saw me in Kansas City?"

"Yeah. You looked-"

"Sad?"

"Uh, yeah."

She smiles and stretches her arms over her head. She moves methodically, like she's taken a yoga class. Or a hundred yoga classes.

"Boy trouble," she says, allowing her arms to fall back into her lap.

I pull at the strap of my backpack, not sure how to proceed. I want to know about the boy trouble this pretty person is in, but I don't want to seem like I want to know the boy trouble this pretty person is in.

"Want to talk about it?" I ask. Then I shake my head. "Sorry, that made me sound like your psychologist. Or your dad."

"Equally creepy," she says. "But sure. I mean, if you want to hear a break-up story."

I sit, one gray modular airport chair between us.

"Tell me everything," I say, plopping my backpack on the thin, gray airport carpet.

So she does. And it *is* sad. She's in school at Arizona State, but before that she was at a small college in Nebraska. Which is where he is. They tried the distance thing for a while, and it seemed like it was working. Until it wasn't.

I consider asking if his name is Dustin and if he ever had a pen pal in Kansas, but settle on a different question.

"Did he see it coming?"

"Well, kind of. But he still wasn't happy."

"I guess we never are, when we're getting broken up with."

"Sounds like someone with experience."

I look up at the gate. Our flight to Phoenix is delayed by

twenty minutes, which means I'm a few hours and twenty minutes away from signing a contract with the NBA's Phoenix Suns. I sort of couldn't believe it, when my agent called two days before this. I was at my parents' house, having left Russia and the girl who showed me the Söyembikä Tower. I had no plan in place, except that I wanted to open the Christmas presents I'd missed for the sixth consecutive year.

And that maybe I was done playing basketball.

Then again, I sort of *could* believe it, when my agent called two days before this. I'd always suspected this would happen, if I kept moving, kept pushing, and didn't let myself get stuck anywhere, or with anyone.

2

Avrio

On the day appointed for the first payment of my professional basketball career, my new team's manager showed up before practice with envelopes for everyone—envelopes stuffed with cash.

This was mildly inconvenient, largely because the manager, Stelios, gave us the cash *before* practice and it wasn't like we had lockers where we could stow our money. Our locker room was a 15' x 15' bunker with two long wooden benches that sat in a stew of used shower water, sweat, and toe fungus.

Only two weeks before this, I'd been in training camp with the defending World Champion Los Angeles Lakers. We'd flown to training camp in a chartered jet. In training camp, I'd had an entire time-share apartment to myself. Oh, and training camp was in Hawaii.

This was a long way from Hawaii.

I jammed the puffy envelope into one of the shoes I'd worn to practice and was pleasantly surprised afterward when I found that neither my shoes nor my money was gone. The next day, I duly deposited the money in my new Greek bank account and fired up Microsoft Money, where a little bar graph told me that I was basically a member of the *nouveau riche*.

And, officially, a professional basketball player.

I'd had my doubts. After my release by the Lakers, I'd decamped to my parents' basement, making mid-morning trips to my old high school gym where I worked out under the watchful eye of my middle school PE teacher. I could see the doubt in my other former teachers' eyes as they peeked through the gym doors.

Professional basketball player? Riiiiight.

My teachers hadn't been the only ones who were worried. My parents didn't say anything, but I could sense their impatience blooming like the thistles that grew in our pasture. Basketball had been cute in college, but wasn't it time to start thinking about My Future?

Then my agent called. A team in Greece wanted to sign me. But, like, immediately. I was supposed to fly to Athens the day after they made the offer. When I'd imagined playing basketball in Europe, I'd imagined something more measured—a leisurely flight to the city in question, where over an upscale dinner the coaches would try to convince me that I was just the player they needed. They'd show me where I'd live. I'd ask pointed questions about playing time. My agent and I would weigh the pros and cons of the contract and *then* I would decide. I mean, I'd never even been to Europe, and now a team was asking me to come spend the rest of the year there, sight unseen?

There was one other problem. The team from Greece had called exactly five days before Darin Densmore's wedding, and I was supposed to be Darin's best man.

I called Darin, and Darin told me I was going to miss his wedding. He said it was time for me to go see some of the places we'd told the audience about back in third grade, when he'd been the narrator and I'd been Pablo in Jefferson West Elementary School's production of *Pablo the Reindeer*.

Darin had one condition: I had to promise to do my best to make him proud with the female population of Greece.

I told him I'd try, even though girls were just about the furthest thing from my mind. I was far more concerned with proving I wasn't crazy for thinking I could make it as a professional athlete.

My first games under the employ of Panionios Basketball Club were marked by three- or four-minute bursts, during which I would invariably do something my coaches loved before invariably doing something they hated, at which point I was yanked in favor of one of my teammates. We had two Greek stars—a power forward who favored fadeaway jumpshots and a guard who drove a

Porsche and played like it. At center was a friendly American who would die following a suspicious heart attack a few years after his career ended. Our shooting guard was a 34-year-old Bosnian with a nose like a tomahawk and a temper like a Tomahawk missile. And our point guard was a Frenchman who, if you watch the video of Vince Carter dunking over Frederic Weis in the 2004 Olympics, can be seen trying to take the ball out of bounds with a very surprised look on his face.

When I arrived, the team was still trying to justify the big contract that tethered it to the Greek big man who was three years and ten kilos past his prime. I was the scissors, waiting in the junk drawer. The big Greek knew his days were (potentially) numbered and showed occasional signs that he might be turning a corner, participating in such uncharacteristic activities as passing the ball and showing up to practice on time. But then, in a game on the home court of perennial Greek basketball powerhouse Olympiacos, our first-year coach lit into him for failing to run back on defense. His pride hurt, the big Greek stormed past the bench and straight into the locker room.

Our coach grabbed me by the shoulder and pushed me toward the scorer's table.

We didn't win the game, but I could tell things were about to change by the way my team played when I was in the game, which is to say: better. And then, as we walked off the court after a loss that was not as bad as it should have been and as I was congratulating myself on my ascent into the lineup, someone in the crowd chucked a bottle of water at my head.

I ducked just in time.

The big Greek still came to practice after that, but he would never really play for us again. It was just the catalyst the team needed. We could handle playing with one prima donna— the Porsche driver. And that prima donna, alerted by the way things had gone for his comrade-in-arms, shaped up, too. The five of us were backed up by a Greek power forward who would, years later, be taken for all he was worth by a model from Eastern Europe and a Greek guard named Marios, which I always thought was a weird name for a Greek person.

We had no real shot at one of the first three spots in the standings, held down by teams with budgets that were six or seven times the size of ours. Panathinaikos was the favorite to win it all; they paid one player $2 million a year. Olympiacos and its squad of veterans was expected to come next. Then came AEK, a team that shared a home court with Panathinaikos. All three teams were bearing the torch of Greece's basketball tradition, which had always burned bright but which had gotten even brighter in the mid-1990s, around the time NBA Hall of Famer Dominique Wilkins signed to play with AEK. Videos from the era show fans packed into 12,000-seat arenas, cheering with the sort of fervor usually reserved for 21st century soccer matches and 17th century beheadings. This being all the more remarkable when one considers the demographics. Twelve million people live in Greece. There were 14 teams in the Greek first division. At various times, six of those teams could have been considered world-class. It was like the city of Chicago supporting six NBA teams and another eight minor league teams.

In addition to our slate of regular-season Greek games, we were one of 32 teams from all over Europe playing for the Saporta Cup, the international basketball league just beneath the Euroleague. Every other week, we'd fly to a new European city. In Istanbul, I learned just how much the Greeks hate the Turks when the coaching staff took me to see the old Greek monuments in "Constantinople" but wouldn't let me go to the Blue Mosque. In Madrid, we stayed near Real Madrid's stadium, and I marveled at the way my usually xenophobic teammates worshiped the ground there. After our game in Le Mans, my teammates said they were going to a brothel. I assumed they were joking because I didn't think real people went to brothels. They weren't joking. And no, I didn't go along. Gross.

It was a dizzying introduction to professional basketball, to Europe, and to professional basketball in Europe. But I could tell by the way the coaches were treating me that I was getting along just fine. They talked about how, if I wanted to, I could probably become one of the best American players in Europe. After three years playing for a college coach who took every opportunity to tell me (and my teammates) how we'd probably never amount to anything, their words felt like a cool breeze on an August afternoon, and I wondered if they were onto something. My dreams of becoming a pro had always ended in the NBA.

But back then, I hadn't known that a person could make a living playing in Europe.

I began to imagine a new path. I could stay in Greece for a couple of years and then upgrade to Spain, or Italy, or maybe even Turkey. As my career wound down, I'd move to Northern Europe, where the pay was less but the girls were prettier. I'd meet one, we'd get married, and I'd live in Stockholm for the rest of my life.

And then, just as I was coming to terms with my new, simplified destiny, a couple of complications arose, as complications are wont to do.

One of the coaches who was rejiggering my future had also taken it upon himself to educate me in the ways of the world. In a conversation about the Balkans, I learned from Nikos that it was *possible* that my home country wasn't the benevolent world actor I'd been taught to believe. On a day off, he took me to his hometown, where we dodged a sheep stampede and I ate things wrapped in grape leaves.

One day after practice, Nikos found out I had nothing to do on some upcoming Greek holiday. He leaned toward me in the conspiratorial way he had.

"You will come with me and Boga," he said, nodding toward the team's other assistant coach, a bearlike man with a big belly and a bigger laugh.

The next afternoon, Nikos and Boga picked me up at my apartment in Glyfada, and we careened through the streets in Boga's ancient silver Mercedes, Bob Dylan blasting from the speakers. When we arrived at the event, we sat down at the end of a long table that was identical to fifteen others in the room—all of them vaguely situated around a stage where I assumed something involving music would later happen. But before anything could happen onstage, there was food. First, items I could identify. Next, items I could not; something out of Dr. Seuss had just been dropped onto my plate.

Watching my reaction, Boga jabbed Nikos, who acted as the team's strength and conditioning coach. He'd been given that title, I think, because he was the only person on staff who didn't smoke. Nikos also spoke flawless English, a product of an undergraduate education at Columbia University. This meant he was theoretically capable of explaining what food had been put in front of me.

"Just try it. Then I'll tell you," he said.

I shrugged and put it in my mouth, which is a statement that never leads anywhere good.

My "food" tasted like what you might imagine Jabba the Hutt's testicles would taste like, in case you've ever imagined what Jabba the Hutt's testicles would taste like.

Nikos explained that what I'd just eaten was a combination of one section of a pig's innards stuffed into another section of a pig's innards.

I groaned, predictable grossed-out American.

"Don't worry!" he said. "*Bouzoukia* isn't only about the food!"

You've probably seen *bouzoukia* on TV or in a movie—those parties where Greeks smash plates and throw roses and drink copious amounts of ouzo. In person, *bouzoukia* are exactly like you'd imagine, except that you also kind of fear for your life because the plates and the roses are thrown with little concern for their ultimate destination.

All this dancing and singing and shouting and inaccurate throwing gave me cover to have a good look around the party. It didn't take me long to spy a table of girls off to one side.

At a pause in the pageantry, I asked Nikos about them. He smiled in that self-satisfied Greek manner—the same manner I'd seen employed whenever Greeks started boasting about how they'd invented Western civilization—and told me "those girls" were the Greek national rhythmic gymnastics team. I would learn later that the Greek national rhythmic gymnastics team is no great shakes at rhythmic gymnastics. But on this night, I was ready to assume that I was looking at a bunch of gold medalists. I hadn't even kissed a girl since I'd left college nine months before.

I nodded at the tallest girl in the group, which might strike you as impossible considering that the girls were all seated, but that's only because you are not 6'9" and accustomed to figuring out at a glance how tall people are.

"What about that one?"

"Ahhh! You like her, eh?" Nikos said.

"Well, I don't know, maybe a little, I mean, she looks pretty goo-"

Nikos turned to Boga.

"Paul likes one of the gymnasts!"

"Yes?" Boga said.

I nodded. Or half-nodded. More of a shrug, probably.

"Then you must dance with her!"

I didn't want to seem like a coward in front of these two Greek men (which is another statement that never leads anywhere good), so I herded all of my courage into the area of my brain responsible for talking to strangers and walked over to the girl. My arrival was made cumbersome by the logistics: she was sitting with her friends, and I was looming over all of them like a human Colossus.

"Hi!" I said. "Would you dance with me?"

She responded like anyone would when faced with a stranger who's spewing a foreign language at her: she tried to bore out my eyes with hers and said, "What?"

As my little courage minions began to look at one another with unease, hoping for the order to retreat, I crouched onto my haunches.

"I don't know anyone here. Will you rescue me?"

When the unibrowed DJ who'd been channeling Prince for most of the night played his last song, I looked up from the stage at the front of the room to find both Boga and Nikos beaming at me. Their evident approval felt like vindication. When we'd left my apartment, I'd been afraid I would revert to my old fourth grade ways, unable to adapt to whatever odd situation they were going to put me in. But I'd done better than adapt—I'd thrived!

And danced!

There was only one obstacle left: I had to get her number. As any man knows, it doesn't matter how well you've connected with the girl you've met at the bar—how many secrets you've shared, how much you have in common, how little you like a particular rock band that everyone else loves—if you can't bring back her phone number, you've failed.

"So, could we go out sometime, just the two of us?"

I assumed that my request was a formality. I mean, she wouldn't have danced with me for so long and with such ferocity in her eyes if she wasn't planning to give me her number.

Right?

"Give me *your* number," she said, her chin jutting out like an attorney who smells blood in the witness stand.

I tracked down a napkin and a pen and I wrote the phone number of my Athens apartment on it. I gave it to her with what I hoped was a friendly smile, saying something overly formal, as if I'd just finished a job interview: "I shall look forward to her call."

Then I went back to Boga and Nikos and we got into the silver Mercedes.

As we pulled into the warren of Athenian streets, and with Barry White crooning at 112 decibels, Nikos turned in the front seat, that knowing grin on his face.

"So, did you get her number?"

When I shook my head no, he and Boga confirmed my suspicion: it wasn't just American males who will ridicule a friend for failing to secure a girl's phone number.

"She'll call!" I said.

They laughed. And they laughed. And they laughed.

But for once, they were wrong!

Demetra did call, around the time I'd forgotten about her entirely.

"Sorry," she said. "I was busy."

As we spoke, I confirmed something I'd feared when I met her on the dance floor but which at the time I'd chalked up to the usual conversational hindrances found on a dance floor (noise, chaos, roses, plates): Demetra knew something like 300 words of English. In any other country, I might have been able to combat her linguistic deficiencies with a contribution of my own—maybe, say, a few hundred words of Greek in my lexical battery. But the thing about Greek is that it is *hard*. I knew the words for "thank you," "water," "please," and "a little." Also, I could count to ten, thank you a little.

But did I mention she was really pretty? Or that I hadn't had sex in about a year?

I wasn't going to let this opportunity slip by. I asked Demetra to go to a movie with me, thinking the screen would mitigate some of our conversational difficulties. And sure enough, it did. And, as I learned after the movie, having only a few words at your disposal is a little like having only a few Legos in your box:

sometimes you actually build a better spaceship in spite of your material pauperhood.

Anyway, did it really matter if we were incapable of replicating *Before Sunrise?* She was 19 and thinking about medical school in Switzerland. I was 24 and at the start of a wildly successful professional basketball career that was going to take me all over the world!

My second payment as a member of the Panionios Basketball Club inspired the same behavior as the first: receive cash, put cash in shoe, take cash to bank, gloat at how I was never going to have to worry about money again.

The third, though—well, the third payment was a problem.

You might have thought I'd gotten a hint that things were about to go awry when I saw Stelios's face that day. But Stelios always looked a little downcast, as if Charlie Brown grew up and turned Greek. So it wasn't until Stelios handed over the envelope that I knew something was amiss. I could tell the envelope was light. Literally—it didn't weigh enough.

I cocked an eyebrow in the way of a 24-year-old who's not yet sure he should be cocking eyebrows at anyone.

"*Avrio,*" Stelios said. "Paul, we have the rest *avrio.*"

"What is *avrio?*"

"It means, uh...tomorrow! Yes, tomorrow!"

Around this time, vandals had broken out two of the enormous windows that made up the wall opposite the bleachers inside our gym. Winter in Greece isn't cold by Midwestern American standards, but neither is it exactly warm.

Stelios told us the team didn't have enough money to replace the windows or pay for the oil required by the heater in our gym. Soon enough, my teammates and I were donning stocking caps for practice.

A funny thing happened when the team stopped paying us in full: nothing really changed. Oh, practice took on a more whimsical tone. Whenever one of us was asked to do something he didn't like, he shouted, "Or what? You won't pay us?"

But it wasn't like we stopped trying to win. In fact, our nonpayment became something of a common enemy, like we were the Cleveland Indians in *Major League*, hoping to get back at their owner by pulling the team out of the cellar.

As the partial payments and the accompanying promises of *avrio* continued, we kept rising through the standings in the Greek league, whose games we played on weekend nights as a contingent of riot police large enough to stop a terrorist cell looked on. Greek fans threw stones, chairs, or, as I knew, water bottles at players. They treated each other even worse; in one game between Panathinaikos and Olympiacos, fans of one team shot Roman candles at their counterparts across the court. I heard rumors that part of the reason the Greeks didn't like the Euro, which had been introduced on New Year's, was that the currency's biggest coin was about a quarter the weight of an old 100-drachma coin—a much better projectile thanks to its heft.

Faced with an explanation of my troubles with Panionios's policy of salary (non)payment, my agent explained that Greek law doesn't protect the employee if he withholds his services. In other words, if I went on the one-man strike I was considering, my contract would be voided.

Ours wasn't the only conversation happening on the subject of employee/employer relations. I was hearing complaints from all over the league. Because each team was only allowed two Americans (to keep the league from being overwhelmed by muggles), we almost always talked before and after games, sometimes even meeting for dinner at the Athens TGI Friday's, a restaurant I wouldn't be caught dead in while in America, but one that was as welcome as a Ziploc full of Hot Tamales when I was so far from home.

The stories seemed like something out of *Catch-22*. So-and-so hadn't gotten paid in three months! The whole AEK team is thinking about going on strike! Yeah, well, that other guy I know got his whole check!

Then, one Friday night, I heard a knock on the door of my apartment. My landlord was standing in my hallway.

"You must be out of apartment tomorrow," he said. "Your team has not paid rent."

My stomach turned over like it had when I'd eaten the pig entrails at the *bouzouki* club. I couldn't imagine what I'd do if I had to leave my apartment. Ordering *souvlaki* by myself was hard. Finding an apartment would be impossible.

I told the landlord I would look into the situation and called Stelios, already imagining what I would do if I had to move all my things out of the apartment in the morning. Would I be in charge of finding my own place? Could I even get an apartment without the work permit I was supposed to have? Would Demetra help me move? You had to be pretty strong to be a rhythmic gymnast, right?

Breathlessly, I told Stelios what was happening.

He waited for me to finish and then asked, "This is all?"

"Uh, yeah," I said. "He's going to kick me out of here if you don't pay the rent!"

Then Stelios laughed, and laughed, and laughed—a common Greek reaction to most problems, I was finding.

"Paul," he said. "Relax. Greek law will protect the person in the apartment until he is six months behind. Tell this landlord he should not get so nervous."

I probably should have taken those words as a harbinger of things to come, but for now, I was going to channel my inner Greek. After all, I wasn't going on strike. And it looked like I still had a place to live, even if any and all future encounters with my landlord were going to be contentious at best.

So I continued to play basketball. I continued to wait for *avrio*. And I continued to see Demetra. Sure, the conversations we had weren't going to be held up by the United Nations as models of international cooperation, but so what? Maybe we could make up for our lack of conversation with a copious amount of copulation.

Yeah, that's the ticket.

One afternoon, we were fooling around on the low-slung bed in my guest bedroom. It was the afternoon because Demetra lived at home with her 72-year-old father, her 49-year-old mother (way to go, Pops!), and her 21-year-old sister. So I had to have her home by ten. Or rather: I had to drop her off at a spot around the corner from her home by ten. Her father, she said, hated Americans, and she hadn't told him about me, wasn't planning to tell him about me, and the best way to keep him from knowing about me was for me to drop her off two blocks from her house.

As to why we were in the guest bedroom: that I can't explain. I just felt like it was going to waste.

Whatever. The point is: we were getting down to... something, and Demetra finally slipped a hand down my pants. Until this revelation, we'd kept it strictly middle-school. Replete, even, with her batting away my hand anytime I tried to put it up her shirt.

Demetra did some fumbling down there and it wasn't exactly smooth and pleasure-packed but after a while-

OK, honestly, if you're a 24-year-old male who hasn't had sex in a year and a pretty Greek girl with an ~~Olympic~~ Pan Am Games body is touching your penis, you're going to get off. You could be in a cave full of spiders and you'd come. And that's what I did. All over her hand, the guest bed, and my stomach. And that was lovely. I mean, as lovely as any handjob can be, which is more like Not Terrible.

Until it wasn't, because Demetra wasn't stopping. And you don't have to be a 24-year-old male to know that that hurts. What you do have to be is someone who's never given a job, hand- or otherwise, before.

Demetra was a virgin.

So here was a quandary. On the one hand, it didn't seem kosher to come to Greece and deflower this very nice girl I only sorta knew. Also, her father might kill me.

On the other hand: biology.

I consoled myself with the amount of time I had left: probably another month, depending on how we did in the Greek league and the Saporta Cup.

I kept seeing Demetra and we kept making out (although I put an end to the handjobs). Our campaign for the Saporta Cup ended in Poland, where we couldn't muster the 11-point loss we needed to advance to the semifinals. (The requirements for advancement were very confusing.)

On the domestic side, we finished in fifth place, good enough to qualify for a first-round playoff series against a rising Greek star who would one day give the American national team fits in the Olympics. After fighting to a standstill, we lost the pivotal fifth game and went home to Athens. We had one last practice, which I thought was odd until I showed up and we played a game of indoor soccer. A picture of me exists from that day: my hair grown out for the first time in my life (I had curls!), my arms around Marios and Nikos and Boga.

I was tired and run down after my first year as a professional basketball player. But no matter, the fact remained that I *was* a professional basketball player. Or at least, half of one. That we'd qualified for the playoffs had qualified me for a $5,000 bonus. Which meant Panionios Basketball Club was on the proverbial hook for $105,000 for the year.

I'd been paid $52,000—just under 50% of what I was owed.

Technically, the team still had the option to employ me the following year. I couldn't imagine how I would ever come back to Greece after the team's careless attitude toward contract law, but my agent told me to act like I might return; it would help our efforts in getting me paid. Efforts that would be aided further by his arrival in Athens. He had plenty of reason to come to town. Not only was Panionios in arrears with me, but my agent represented players on those other teams all over the country—teams who had, like mine, finished the year owing money to their players.

I stayed in my apartment for a few extra days, hoping for a miracle—a miracle that, it was soon clear, wasn't likely to happen. Two days into his stay, my agent explained that we were going to have to sue the team for my money, and suing the team wouldn't exactly endear me to that team.

If *avrio* ever arrived, it wasn't going to be soon.

It was time to go home.

And it was time to tell Demetra.

The beach in Athens isn't beautiful. It's rocky and a little scuzzy; I learned while I lived there that only in the mid-1970s did someone decide that pumping the city's raw sewage directly into the Aegean wasn't a good idea. But still, it's as good a place as any in Athens for a romantic good-bye stroll. So, after a mediocre lunch, Demetra and I set off, chattering away in our small-vocabularied way.

It took me a mile and a half to get to:

"So it looks like this is good-bye, huh?"

I assumed we'd spend the rest of the walk talking about how much fun we'd had in the months we'd been together, figure out how best to stay in touch, and then maybe, just maybe, I would be able to steer this conversation toward us going back to my apartment for one, last hedonistic night.

That's right, I was thinking about sex when Demetra said, "What?"

Maybe she'd misunderstood. It happened about 80% of the time.

"The team isn't going to pay me. So I have to go home."

I pointed out at the sea, like 'home' was on the island of Crete.

"So?"

"Uhhh, so," I stammered. "I leave on Monday."

"So?"

Why did she keep saying 'so'?

"Um, so, we need to, er, break up."

And that's when she broke down. Like, started crying, obviously, but also falling onto me like an Italian woman who's just learned that her eldest son has died in a hail of Allied gunfire. A part of me was flattered, that I meant so much to this lovely Greek rhythmic gymnast with the best name of anyone I'd ever dated, or will ever date. Another part of me was disappointed; I didn't know much about women, Greek or otherwise, but I did know that hysteria is not usually a precursor to sex.

Most of me, however, was mortified. It was a Saturday afternoon and it was mid-May after a winter that had brought a rare snowstorm to Athens. There were people *everywhere*. And what that meant was that I spent the next hour half-dragging, half-carrying to my car a nineteen-year-old Greek girl who, every five steps, would be overcome by paroxysms of grief or despair or confusion, while simultaneously apologizing with my eyes to Greek person after Greek person, each of whom must have assumed that I'd just told my girlfriend that not only was I not going to stick around for the kid, we were going for the abortion RIGHT THE FUCK NOW.

Eventually, I got Demetra back to my car. I drove her to the neighborhood where her family lived and, after another hour of outlining why our relationship was doomed, we had one last kiss and she got out of my car.

Two blocks from her house, naturally.

Back in my parents' basement, where the memory of Demetra's attempted handjob was becoming less unpleasant with each passing day, I used the dial-up modem to make increasingly frequent checks of my bank account, hoping the money the Greeks owed me would appear. By mid-summer, when I went off to the NBA's summer league for the second time, I'd seen no transfers. But I had hope. My agent said the lawsuit had commenced. It would only be a matter of time, he said.

I played well enough at summer league to warrant a training camp invite from the NBA's Atlanta Hawks, who told me they wanted me to report in early September so I could spend a few weeks working out with the team before camp started. I wasn't overjoyed by the prospect of going to another training camp without a contract. But one look around my parents' basement reminded me that I didn't have many other options.

I got ready to leave for Atlanta.

Then the general manager from Panionios called. I assumed he wanted some bank account info, so the team could send over that sweet cash.

I rubbed my hands together, Daddy Warbucks-style.

"When will you come back?" the general manager asked.

Um, what?

This was the offer he made: if I returned to Athens, the team would wire $20,000 of the $53,000 they owed me. The remaining $33,000 would be spread out over the life of the coming year's payments.

"That's one big *avrio*," I said.

The general manager laughed at my in-joke. Then he said the magic words, his voice low and syrupy.

"Trust me, Paul."

I'd like to say that I hung up immediately. But the truth is that I almost went for it. As strange as my year there had been, Greece was a reassuring constant in the equation representing my basketball career. The Atlanta Hawks, on the other hand, were an ugly, intimidating variable—an x that still needed to be plucked from an unholy polynomial. I didn't have a spot on the team; I'd be fighting for practice time again, just like the year before in camp with the Lakers.

There was one other factor at work: the Greeks' preternatural capacity for salesmanship. There was something about the people—maybe it was their accent, maybe it was their history—that made me *want* to trust them, despite the fact that I'd spent the year getting burned by that trust.

But then I recalled the half-weight envelopes, the stocking caps, and my breakup with Demetra, which had been predicated on the idea that I had to move forward if I was going to have the career I wanted.

"OK," I said. "How about you wire that $53,000, and then we'll talk?"

He refused. And I hung up.

We won the lawsuit my agent helped file. The team appealed our win. We won the appeal. And then, after months and months of misdirection and subterfuge and outright lies, the management at Panionios relented and-

Just kidding.

Because enough teams were in debt, and because so many teams were being sued by players like me, the Greek sports commission made a deal with the teams: they could declare bankruptcy, re-commence operation under different names (my team "changed" its name by adding the year of the team's founding) and their debts would be forgiven, under one oh-so-onerous condition: they had to promise they'd never do it again.

Seven years later, the Greek economy fell to pieces, nearly taking Europe and those too-small Euros with it. In the Greek government's negotiations for a bailout, it arranged for a "haircut" of its debts. Instead of owing its creditors the full amount of their loans, the government agreed to a deal that allowed their responsibility to be slashed by a significant percentage. Specifically, 50%.

I was not surprised by the amount.

"So, what happened with the Atlanta Hawks?"

This is not the question I expected the girl in the Memphis airport to ask. It is, though, a question that shows she's been paying attention, and so I am pleased with myself. I have kept her entertained for the duration of our delay, and this might mean a date when we get to Phoenix.

"I didn't make it," I say, shaking my head for effect.

"Ah, damn," she says.

I hold up both forefingers and grin.

"I mean, not the first time. But later that season, after I'd been playing in the CBA—that's a minor league—for three months, they signed me to a ten-day contract."

"So it worked!"

"It did," I say. "Although I guess that's not really what I took from it."

"And what, pray tell, did you take away from it?"

She folds her arms across her chest and leans back in the gray chair to await the wisdom I have to dispense.

"For one, that *avrio* doesn't really mean 'tomorrow.'"

"I picked up on that. And?"

"And, if you're going to break up with someone, do it at the end of your walk, not the beginning."

She huffs a laugh.

"Yeah, that was a rookie move. But you were, what, 23?"

"Twenty-four, but yeah."

The gate agent begins a call for first class passengers to board—the universal indicator that we should gather our things. I look at the gate, then back at her.

"Do you want to hear the last thing?"

She glances at the gate.

"Sure."

"Well," I say, knowing I don't have long. "I knew I was leaving, one way or another. Even if I came back for another season, that was going to be the beginning of what I hoped was going to be a long basketball career and what was, for sure, going to be an unpredictable basketball career. I should have made that clear to Demetra. So I got a $53,000 reminder in how to treat girls."

She weighs what I've said with narrowed eyebrows.

"I don't know about all that," she says, leaning forward to pull her messenger bag across the low carpet.

"No?"

"You said she was going to be, what, a med student?"

"Yeah."

She stands, slinging her bag over her shoulder. She's looking down at me like my father used to look at the chickens he was considering buying at the swap meets in the little town south of Topeka.

"Give her a little credit. She knew what was going on. Or she should have."

I look up at her, a rare event for me.

"So I'm forgiven?"

"Sure. Especially because that was the first time it dawned on you."

"What dawned on me?"

"That you could have a girlfriend or a basketball career, but not both."

I rub my eyes with the palm of my hand. She has cut to the core of it.

But I have come this far.

"So," I say. "Want to get a drink in Phoenix?"

She fixes me with a stare as she hikes the messenger bag onto her shoulder one last time.

I can feel the grin pulling at the corners of my mouth.

"No? This close to the end of things with the guy in Nebraska?"

"Yeah," she says. "That."

She hits me with a finger gun as she walks away. And I decide that in another life, we'd get along just fine.

PHOENIX
A Wednesday night

I yelp and she asks what has just happened.

There's alarm in her voice, but not a lot. There aren't many things that could have gone wrong between the bed and the trash can.

"It hurts a little, taking them off."

She covers her face with her hands and shakes her head, haloing her long hair against the pillow in a way that's going to leave her with a serious case of the Twists & Tangles.

Now it's my turn to ask.

"What?"

"Nothing," she says. "They're just funny. Condoms, I mean."

I stretch out across her stomach, which is a really great stomach. Like, the sort of stomach you see in ads for expensive blue jeans.

I had a feeling this would be the case the first time I saw her. She was helping one of the photographers stationed at the end of our bench and she had on the coolest shoes: pink Pumas that seemed suited perfectly for work on the periphery of a basketball court. Not that her shoes had anything to do with her stomach.

But surely one of my teammates had already asked her out, or worse. And if they had, that was curtains for me. I couldn't compete with Steve Nash or Amar'e Stoudemire or Shawn Marion. I couldn't even compete with Jake Voskuhl, mired at the end of the bench like I was. Then there was the proximity thing. Like, what if I asked for her number and she said no and then we were stuck seeing each other every home game for the rest of the year?

Then one of our assistant coaches swooped in like a good-natured *deus ex cupida*. He saw me eyeing her during warm-ups and walked right over. He came back with her number and her news.

"She thinks you're cute. She said to call her."

So I did, thinking all the while that maybe this was going to be like that time at one of my brother's baseball games when this grimy kid from Perry came over to where I was sitting on the bleachers. He asked me if I could see the girl at the top of the stands on the other side. When I said yes, he said she'd told him she wanted to talk to me. As soon as I got to the top of the bleachers, the truth was confirmed for me by the way the dirty kid from Perry was doubled over in laughter at the bottom of the bleachers.

But it was not like Perry, where the girl at the top of the bleachers looked at me like I had an eye in the middle of my forehead when I pointed at the grimy kid and said he'd told me she wanted to talk to me.

The girl with the pink Pumas was glad I'd called, she said. We went out once, twice, and now this: her in my bed in the short-term rental apartment an assistant general manager helped me find, telling me condoms are funny.

From my vantage point on her beautiful stomach, I twist my head so I can look up at her.

"You don't know the half of it," I say.

3

Let's Talk About Sex (Baby)

One day at the beginning of seventh grade home economics, our matronly teacher Mrs. Bohannon told the twenty-five of us assembled that we would be taking a break from learning how to cook.

It was Sex Ed Day.

On cue, a tall, neatly-dressed woman walked through the door to the Home Ec. classroom, her graying hair lending an air of authority to an already-authoritative stride. She had come from the county health department to warn my fellow pubescents and me of the perils of sexual intercourse—pregnancy, AIDS, and various other outcomes that would leave our lives as ruined as one of the funnel cakes that Group 6 had left in the oil too long the day before.

I shifted uncomfortably in my chair as the woman from the health department arranged herself behind the podium Mrs. Bohannon had set up at the front of class. I was squirming partly because it was Sex Ed Day, I was in seventh grade, and I was mystified by anything and everything having to do with my female classmates.

But mostly because the Sex Ed teacher was my mother.

Thanks to my mom's role as the county's de facto sex educator at the health department, sex was an open topic in the Shirley household. My mom tested on my brothers and me the videos she was considering using in classrooms. She told us about the nighttime treks she sometimes had to make in order to appear in front of school boards reluctant to allow her to talk to their districts' students about birth control. On a memorable drive to a baseball game, she explained to us, her sons, how it was that anal sex increased the chances of HIV transmission. (More ripping and tearing of tissue, duh.)

I didn't enjoy any of this home-based sexual education. I knew none of my friends were enduring anything like it. And when you're in seventh grade, all you really care about is whether what you're doing is the same as what everyone else is doing.

I stared at the chalkboard in front of me as my mother rolled—or unrolled, if we're going for accuracy here—an unlubricated Trojan on the penis-shaped protrusion made by her index and middle fingers. When she was finished, she held up the two-fifths of her left hand that were encased in latex, doing so with a little more pride than I would have liked.

And that's when it happened. From about three people to my left, Justin Bridges said, "Too bad Paul's never going to get to do that, huh?"

At age 13, the furthest I'd advanced with anyone of the opposite sex was a running commentary with my longstanding crush, Lisa Zerr, about how we both loved *Doogie Howser, M.D.*, which was the television show that made Neil Patrick Harris famous for people of my generation, before Neil Patrick Harris was made famous by an entirely different television show for people of another generation.

Justin Bridges was hardly any teenaged lothario, either. He had, though, made significant advances on the dual fronts of body odor and hair in weird places. Oh, and confidence. He had plenty of that, too.

As Justin was looking around for approval from my classmates, many of whom were my friends, but none of whom was immune to a good joke about a coward, my mother, bless her heart, looked to Mrs. Bohannon. She did this because she knew stepping in on her son's behalf would only make things worse, probably in the form of further ridicule directed at me later in the day.

Mrs. Bohannon felt no such qualms about speaking up.

"Hey!" she said. "Leave him alone!"

This I heard, but did not see. Because when Justin loosed his barb, I raised my arms over my head and looked up at my hands. This seemingly unorthodox move had two functions. One, by looking upward, the tears that were puddling in my eye sockets might, potentially, stay there. And two, because my arms were framing my face, I could hide said tears from my classmates. But when Mrs. Bohannon came so willingly to my defense, all was lost; the tears breached the levees provided by the outer reaches of my orbital bones. In an effort to give cover to my evident distress, my mother asked, again, if there were any questions about her talk, which had included not only the condom demonstration, but also a vigorous and wide-ranging discussion of the many dreadful outcomes of unprotected sex (in the form of slides portraying the types of sores found on genitals infected with syphilis or Chlamydia).

There were not any questions, because in a group of seventh-graders, no one is going to ask sex questions. An awkward silence reigned over the classroom until, mercifully, the bell rang and I squeezed free of my desk like it was my overbearing Aunt Sharon. I sprinted for the door, desperate to get into the hallway, where I could stand in front of my locker, pretend to organize my Trapper Keeper, and hope an earthquake would destroy my middle school and everyone in it, including me (but not including my mother). This would have been a strange thing to have happen in Northeast Kansas, but whatever, this is how imaginations work.

At my locker, I took a deep breath, and then another, and then another, and by the midpoint of the four-minute passing period, my desire to have the school pulverized by an act of the God had dissipated.

I thought I'd made it. But my gauntlet was not yet finished.

Because the town where I grew up was so small, everyone knew everything about everyone else. They also knew that each family had a specific role to play in the ecosystem that made up the social circles in Meriden, Kansas. The Haverkamps were lake people: they had a boat and an F-150 to haul it around. The Phalens were baseball people: their kids played for teams in our county's Little League program *and* for teams in Topeka. The Bridges were poor as dirt: they lived near the grain elevator and their daughter would grow up to be slutty, perhaps because of their socioeconomic struggles or maybe in spite of them.

My family was the one with three tall, skinny boys who read books and played sports. Stairsteps. Me, then two years, then my brother Dan, then two more years, then my brother Matt.

The End.

Until one late spring night when our parents called the first family meeting in the history of our family and broke the news that the population at Rural Route 1, Box 125, was about to grow by 20%. I went immediately into a tailspin whose severity was rivaled only by Darth Vader's TIE Fighter at the end of *Star Wars*. How could my parents do this? We had a good thing going; why mess it up?

I thought this way because I was an eleven-year-old boy and a self-absorbed asshole, like most eleven-year-old boys. My main concern was that I didn't know *anyone* with four kids in their family. Now *we* were going to be the family with four kids, like old-timey farmers or Mormons.

I had a feeling there would be other repercussions as well.

That premonition proved true a few days after my mother's appearance in Home Ec.

"Wait a second," Justin Bridges said, one of his feet propped up on the bench in the middle school locker room—another place I dreaded back then, thanks to my pale skin's tendency to get blotchy, which sometimes compelled my locker mates to accuse me of allowing my father to beat me before school.

Justin ran a hand through hair that was already getting long. In high school, it would stretch to his shoulders, draping across the BRIDGES on the back of his football uniform. Then his eyes took on a rare, laser-like focus.

"Your mom's not very good at practicing what she preaches, now is she?"

There were numerous holes in Justin's logic, like that my parents weren't exactly the people to whom my mother was referring when she suggested caution and care when it came to sexual intercourse. They'd proven themselves at least reasonably capable of providing a nurturing environment for the rearing of small humans. And Justin's remark was hardly timely. A year and a half had elapsed between the birth of my youngest brother and his realization that my mother taught Sex Ed.

However, logic and locker rooms are not natural bedfellows.

The insults came in faster than I could deal with them, like that moment in Missile Command when you know your bases are toast.

"I wonder if he could hear them going at it!"

"I bet he liked it!"

"I bet he taped it! Did you tape it, Paul? Do you watch the replay and beat off?"

I stayed quiet, trying for half-hearted smiles as I felt the tears welling up once again. Why did my mother have to be the one who taught Sex Ed? Why had my parents gotten pregnant again? Why was I letting this bother me so much? More important: why couldn't I just stick up for myself, somehow? Like, more than saying, "Shut up, guys!"

(Which is about the worst thing you can say, if you're a seventh-grade boy.)

The answer was that I wasn't ready to stick up for myself. This was true for exactly the same reason that Justin Bridges was right when he'd said what he'd said when my mother had been standing in front of our class, elbow-deep in a latex sleeve.

In high school, my path diverged from Justin's path. While I was worrying about SOHCAHTOA, he was out in the shop with the portion of the football team that drank Natural Light out of cans and went fishing on weekends. I didn't think we'd buried the hatchet, mostly because I no longer thought about the hatchet.

I'd forgotten about the hatchet!

Then, a few years after high school graduation, Justin Bridges sat down next to me in the back room of a Topeka tavern that was hosting the twenty people (out of a possible 55) who'd come for an impromptu high school reunion. And in that moment, the hatchet came whipping back toward me—what he'd said in Sex Ed., what he'd said in the locker room. Now, though, I could do something about it. Since leaving high school, I'd turned into a giant. I could probably bench-press two adult Justins (or four seventh-grade Justins). I wasn't afraid of a confrontation with Justin Bridges. More important: I'd learned a thing or two about how to carry myself in social situations. For example, I knew I could gather the assembled reunioners and ask if anyone remembered

Sex Ed. day and then point at Justin and say, "Remember how this asshole said I was never going to have sex? Well, I *have* had sex. And more than once!"

OK, maybe I hadn't learned *that* much about how to carry myself in social situations.

On a tentative search for a topic of conversation, I asked Justin about the family I knew he had. Families were already becoming *de rigueur* for my high school classmates; it was a question I'd already used on two others in attendance.

He said it was OK, ups and downs.

Then he shook his head.

"Can you believe it? I already have three kids."

"Wow," I said. "That's a lot of kids."

"I know," he said. "Oldest is six." When he saw what happened to my eyes when he said this, he added, "Yeah, we got married five years ago."

I raised an eyebrow. Justin squinted at me. Then his face cracked into a smile. "You were always good with numbers, Shirley."

He raised his beer in salute.

"Maybe I should have paid a little more attention to your mom."

I smiled, allowing myself to breathe as Justin tipped back his can of Miller Lite, finishing it in one gulp.

"But that's not the half of it," he said. "I just got a vasectomy."

According to signs all over Midwestern highways, a vasectomy can be reversed for $599 (results may vary). And Justin did have his kids, his family, a steady place in a life that he probably more or less liked. But still: a vasectomy? We were 25 years old!

I wasn't sure how to process the news of Justin's reproductive demise, so I nodded toward the bar behind us and asked him if he wanted a beer. He held up his empty Miller Lite and shook it before shrugging a nod. I unraveled my legs from the picnic bench they were around and went to the bar, where I bought Justin Bridges a beer and myself a soda water, and I carried those drinks to the table I'd just left. Someone had taken my seat, so I set the Miller Lite in front of Justin.

I knew this was my moment—my chance to exorcise the demons Justin had birthed in seventh grade by making good on the thrust that was available to me. All I had to do was lean in for a whisper, deploy one sentence, and Justin would know what he'd done to me back then, how much it had hurt, how long it had stuck with me.

Justin noticed the beer in front of him. He gripped it with his right hand, turned over his left shoulder, and held the beer up toward me.

"Thanks, Paul," he said, holding out the Miller Lite for me to tap with my club soda.

Which, after examining the creases next to his eyes, the slump in his back, the yellow at the collar of his shirt, is exactly what I did.

"So, you didn't say anything?"

The photographer's assistant is looking down at me.

I shake my head against her stomach.

I can feel her thinking about what she's going to say next. But instead of saying anything, she takes my hand, runs it up between her breasts, and pulls my finger into her mouth.

And *then* she speaks.

"I think," she says. "It's pretty weird that you brought up your mother just now. But I also think you're about to get back at Justin Bridges."

PHOENIX

A Tuesday night

I reach out to touch the shoulder that's only a few inches from my face. It is a shapely shoulder—a swimmer's shoulder—and it is a place I was getting intimately familiar with, a few seconds before this. We were making out in a movie theater parking lot like teenagers. Necking: this is what they would have called it, if "they" lived in 1956.

Then, though, I pulled away from her (mouth, shoulder, neck) to ask her something that was maybe stupid or maybe sweet but whatever it was, it was what was on my mind.

I asked her if she'd come visit me in Russia, if I went.

And now the question hangs between us, as fragile as a bubble made from string and soapy water.

What led to that question?

That's a little more complicated.

I knew it wasn't going to work out with the photographer's assistant with the pink Pumas when I went back into the bar to find her and she didn't get mad. We were at a post-game event set up by the Suns, and she'd come outside from getting me a club soda to find me talking to another girl. This girl had been stalking me since she'd seen me at some other Suns-based event; she'd waited for the photographer's assistant to leave my side and she'd made her move. This was all new to me—this idea of having two beautiful girls interested in me—so I did what any 27-year-old idiot would do: I tried to get the new girl's phone number before the photographer's assistant came back.

I managed to type in the first two letters (AL) of her name before I was caught.

When I got inside, I was expecting the photographer's assistant to throw her drink at me, or storm off, or demand an apology. We weren't an item, necessarily, but we had come together. And we were planning to leave together.

I was right about that: the photographer's assistant was mad.

At herself.

"I had no right to behave like that," she said. "You don't owe me anything."

But I do! I wanted to say. *That was a shitty thing I just did!*

But such is the power you have when you're on an NBA basketball team.

So it didn't work out with the photographer's assistant, and AL was not a long-term solution, so I went to an awards banquet at the end of the regular season by myself. No matter: I was riding high—a full-fledged (if mostly non-playing) member of the best team in the NBA. And that probably helps explain why I had the confidence to lean into the table next to mine, where two tall girls—one with brown hair and one with black hair—were giggling.

When we started talking, I was immediately smitten by the black-haired one. Naturally, it was the brown-haired one who gave me her number at the end of the night. But after some hemming ("Uh") and some hawing ("so") and some brutal honesty ("I have to tell you, I'm actually more interested in your friend"), I managed the impossible and got the friend's phone number.

Such is the power you have when you're on an NBA basketball team.

We went to dinner once, and she came to some playoff games, and this was all well and good, but those playoffs were spiraling to a close, and I could tell that the way I fit into the Phoenix Suns' long-range plans was that I didn't. And then, sure enough, we lost to the San Antonio Spurs in the Western Conference Finals, and the black-haired girl and I said a chaste good-bye.

Until.

Until.

Until.

Summer passes, and I take the black-haired girl to a movie at one of the 9,000 multiplexes in the Greater Phoenix Area. (Movies are a good way to stay out of the heat. There would be a lot of movie theaters on the planet Mercury, too.)

The Suns have brought me back to Phoenix for what has amounted thus far to a two-day try-out, which is a little insulting, considering I was on the team last year.

Such is the power you don't have when you're *not* on an NBA basketball team.

But, as luck would have it, not only are the Suns having me try out for what is essentially my own job, there are other complicating factors as well.

For one: television.

When I was doing all my non-playing for the Suns, the people in charge of the team's website asked if I would be willing to write down a few notes that they could post on the site, thereby creating one of the "blogs" that were raging across the cybersphere. They'd asked me this, I think, because I had a college degree and looked like I could read. Little did they know I'd been writing about my life since I first arrived in Greece, honing my navel-gazing craft by way of the feedback that comes when your friends and family either email you back or don't.

The blog caught a little steam, and Random House called and asked if I wanted to write a book. Through that process, I got a literary agent. And through *that* process, I got a television agent, and he said, "Why don't you come up with an idea for a TV show?"

I said, "What about, 'Wisecracking 12th Man on NBA Team Exposes What Being in NBA Is Really Like'?"

He said, "That's gold, Jerry! Gold!"

OK, maybe he didn't say that, exactly. But that was the implication, and I flew to Los Angeles and we pitched a TV show to Twentieth Century Fox.

And now they're saying we might get to film the pilot, which is a Big Deal, they tell me.

But that's not the only complicating factor vis-à-vis trying out for my old job-slash-dropping bomb-like questions on black-haired former swimmers who are in my car.

Remember Russia? Well, a Russian team wants me to come back to that country to play for them. It's not the team from the city with the Söyembikä Tower. This team is headquartered outside Moscow.

Their first offer was for $400,000.

When I said no, citing something I'd said when I left Russia six months before— which was that I'd never set foot in Russia again— the offer became $500,000.

Now it's $550,000, which is an amount of money that makes what I'm about to write all the more absurd.

I am considering turning it down. This is true because I am cracking up. I've played for 13 basketball teams in four years, which sounds like a lot on its face but is even more "a lot" when you've been in my brain. Because, see, playing for a basketball team hasn't ever just been a matter of showing up, putting on a uniform, and passing the ball around until someone scores. For me, basketball has also always been about trying to connect emotionally with the people I'm playing with, in the same way that someone would connect emotionally with a new batch of workmates or platoon-mates.

And it is that need to connect, over and over, that has broken me.

Well that, and never having had a girlfriend. It's just like the girl in the Memphis airport said. I'm not a safe bet. I'm 27 and the closest I've come is a Greek girl who spoke 300 words of my language.

And that's what has led me to ask this very pretty former swimmer with black hair if she will come to Russia if I go back.

She tilts her head and looks into my eyes in a way that makes me feel like she might be able to see the back of my skull.

"I'll think about it," she says.

This doesn't sit very well.

"Why can't you just say yes?"

She laughs and pats me on the chest. Thanks to those swimmer's shoulders, it's a little rougher than she intended.

"Because I barely know you. Because you're talking about Russia. Because you don't even know if you're going."

She has me there. I've explained the weird triad of options I'm facing.

I take a breath and look off into the nearly deserted parking lot. There's a black Toyota, its engine running, two people inside.

"You're right," I say. "I'm sorry. I should've known better."

"Well, it's not because I'm not adventurous. It's just-"

It's my turn to smile as I interrupt her.

"No," I say. "I'm not saying it's your fault. I'm saying I should understand this by now."

4

Plandango

At the start of my third year as a professional basketball player, I went to training camp with an NBA team that is no longer named what it was then. They were called the Hornets and they'd moved the season before to New Orleans from Charlotte. This was a year before the creation of a new franchise called the Charlotte Bobcats, two years before Hurricane Katrina forced the New Orleans team to play some of its games in Oklahoma City, and eight years before the New Orleans team returned the Hornets name to the Charlotte franchise, and the team I went to training camp with became the New Orleans Pelicans.

In the NBA, as in life, nothing stays the same.

I wasn't supposed to make the team in New Orleans. I was going, Tim Floyd told me, for the following year. The team had a player a lot like me whose contract was up after the season, and Floyd said I just needed to play well in camp, and maybe he'd be able to get me a contract—a real one—the next summer.

Floyd had been hired to coach the Hornets one year after resigning as head coach of the Chicago Bulls and five years after shaking my hand on a team bus one last time, after his second year as my head coach at Iowa State University.

Many people were surprised when he resurfaced in New Orleans; he'd left Chicago under a cloud of ignominy after shepherding that once-proud franchise from the days of Michael Jordan to the days of Michael Ruffin. I was not one of these surprised people. Since Floyd left Iowa State, I'd played for a man who would be named college coach of the year, a man who would go on to coach the Greek national team, a man who'd already coached the Spanish national team, and a man named Phil Jackson, who some might call the best basketball coach in history.

Coach Floyd knew more about basketball than any of them.

I had a surprise for my former college coach. I wasn't as lost in the Hornets' camp as I'd been in my two prior training camps— one with the Los Angeles Lakers, one with the Atlanta Hawks. In fact, I fit in so well that in Orlando after a preseason game against the Magic, an assistant coach called me over to the hotel bar and said, AND I QUOTE:

"I wish I could take a box-cutter to his Achilles so you could make the team."

This particular assistant coach did not traffic in subtleties. Also, he might have had a couple of whiskeys.

My life was shaping up better than I'd planned, so it was with a little extra spring in my step that, one day after practice, I grabbed a paperback, left my downtown New Orleans hotel room and set off down the street, hoping to find some hidden gem for lunch—someplace that would allow me to feel like I was Experiencing The City.

I wandered through a beaten-up neighborhood that didn't have a reassuring name like the Garden Quarter, watching as men shucked their gloves for lunch break after mornings spent welding and pipefitting—a place as far removed from the tourists lurching down Bourbon Street as I could find.

Soon enough, I spied a likely candidate for lunch: a corner restaurant where the paint on the windows was just cracked enough to make me feel like it hadn't been recently tidied up for tourist consumption.

I went in and asked for a table for one.

I wasn't new to going to strange restaurants by myself. After two years as an itinerant basketball player, I was getting used to doing most everything more like Rob Thomas and less like Matchbox 20. But I hadn't always felt so comfortable. At the beginning of my career, I didn't think too highly of my solo dining trips; I was alone, and being alone was pathetic, and everyone in the restaurant knew this to be so, as reflected in their pitying looks my way. But then, somewhere in the world, a waitress came over and asked, "So, what are you doing here? We're dying to know."

It dawned on me then that some of those pitying looks had actually been quizzical looks. The lone guy in the restaurant is mysterious! Whereas everyone else, I realized, was almost completely predictable. The first date, the birthday party, the anniversary dinner—I knew everything about them, but they knew bupkis about me.

There is another ideal aspect to eating alone: the magical electricity that, under the right conditions, can develop between you and the waitress. She's been dealing with bratty kids and demanding couples all day or night or graduation party. And you, with your simple requests and your mysterious motives, might be a welcome respite.

At that café in New Orleans, my waitress was tall and slender, with freckles and dark brown hair. That hair was falling in a few places from a messy ponytail, and a few strands were stuck to her forehead and neck in spots that were damp from sweat. It was hot and humid and she was playing along with the weather, wearing frayed denim shorts and a tank top that was held together just above her cleavage by a leather bow.

One of the keys to being the Mysterious Patron is, of course, mystery. In my lengthy but haphazard experience in such situations, it doesn't pay to start in with a flirtatious quiz; the poor girl gets that from every traveling salesman and assistant football coach who's ever been through the place.

You gots to play it cool.

Playing it cool shouldn't have been hard this day, because "playing it cool" and "doing nothing" look a lot alike. Or so I told myself as I sat in silence while my waitress set a sweating water glass in front of me and told me she'd be back in a few minutes to check on me.

I wiped my forehead to avoid resembling my water glass, which now sat in a puddle of its own moisture.

Maybe it was the heat, or maybe it was just her.

Either way, a montage began unspooling on the screen in my head…

INT. DIMLY LIT JAZZ CLUB

*The music is around the corner from PAUL and
MARY ANNE (because that had to be her name),
allowing them to talk, as long as they lean
in close.*

                    MARY ANNE

          So, you've been here before?

                        PAUL

          Well, not here, exactly.

                    MARY ANNE

          But to New Orleans?

                        PAUL

          Yeah, in college. But I sort of
          don't remember it all that well.

MARY ANNE puts an arm over the seat behind PAUL.

                    MARY ANNE

          Oh, really? Because I'd say New
          Orleans is a pretty memorable place.

*PAUL takes a slow sip of his drink, to hide a
glance at MARY ANNE's tanned arm.*

                        PAUL

          Well, we came to play the University
          of New Orleans. And on my first play

in the game, I got hit with an
elbow that sent me to the floor with
a concussion that left me nauseous
anytime I looked at a light.

     MARY ANNE

Jeez! You're so tough and manly!

     PAUL
     (feigning nonchalance)

It wasn't that big a deal. I mean,
when I finally could open my eyes,
there was a jagged line in my vision
and on one side of the line things
were blurry, while on the other they
were clear, but whatever, it happens
in basketball.

     MARY ANNE
     (motioning with a finger)

Come here.

MARY ANNE kisses PAUL.

End Scene.

On our second date, we'd go back to her place, all brick
walls and brass bedframes, and after I'd gotten through one wall's
worth of exploration of the knick-knackery she'd hung there, I
would turn around to find her stepping out of her little black
dress, daring me to say something. Then someone featured in the
Hornets' plans for the year would get hurt, mysteriously or not,
and I'd make the opening day roster. Not only that, I'd slide into
the regular rotation when Coach Floyd remembered that I was
the only one he could trust to play anything like defense. I would
become a fan favorite and MARY ANNE would be at every game,

watching with delight as I averaged 6.8 points and 3.7 rebounds per game.

And then MARY ANNE came back to take my order.

While she'd been gone, in addition to daydreaming for us an entire future together, I'd also thought about what I'd say to her. Everything I'd come up with seemed predictable. I could ask her name, but that made me feel like a lecherous old man. ("What's your name, darlin'?")

I could tell her she was pretty, but it wasn't like she didn't know that, what with the way she was wearing those jean shorts.

I settled on simple: I'd ask her what was good to eat, and see if anything developed. I looked up from my menu, trying to pretend that her appearance at the side of my booth hadn't set my right arm to quivering.

"What do you all do best here?"

(The "you all" for purposes of solidarity. Kansas is decidedly not in the South, but sometimes it makes sense to play like it is.)

She considered my question and then used the pencil in her right hand to point at the menu.

"Well, people like the chicken salad on ciabatta."

"Ah, but people like *American Idol*. I want to know what *you* think is best."

She shrugged.

"I like the chicken salad, too."

"I didn't mean that *American Idol* is a bad show. I just meant-"

"Of course it's a bad show."

"Right, obviously. Anyway-"

I looked down at the menu, then back at her.

"Chicken salad it is."

"Great," she said. Then she gathered my menu and told me she'd put in my order.

So much for the brick walls and brass bed frames.

I sipped on my water and looked out the window, where the heat rising from the asphalt shimmered in the afternoon sun. I imagined Mary Anne taking me by the hand in order to explain why she liked the heat in New Orleans.

"It makes me feel so free," she'd probably say.

And with that, I'd probably agree, even if I didn't like the heat at all. Because what heat made me think about was our trips back to her apartment, where you couldn't help but take your clothes off and put on Muddy Waters and-

I decided that when she came back, I would engage a new tactic: silence.

I took the book from where I'd left it to rest on the pleather seat next to me and tried to read.

When the chicken salad sandwich appeared in front of me, I looked up from words I'd now read three times, trying, again, to act like she'd surprised me.

"Oh," I said. "Great."

"Enjoy," she said. And then she walked away.

I looked out the window again. This time I noticed only the trash blowing past.

I consoled myself with the knowledge that I had one last arrow in my quiver. And it was probably just the one that would pierce her heart. I mean, she seemed like the type who would respect the direct approach. And maybe that had been the problem all along: she'd seen through my efforts at obfuscation and was hoping I'd quit messing about like all the other child-men who came into the restaurant.

I needed to ask her on a date.

All plans of a relaxing lunch forgotten, I gobbled down my sandwich and practically threw the salad into my mouth. And just in time, too. Her Check-on-Customer return coincided with my last bite.

"How was it?" she asked.

I wiped my mouth and sent up a prayer to Our Lady of Spinach Between the Teeth.

"It was great," I said, sneaking a deep breath and putting an arm on the back of the booth next to me. "So, here's the thing: I don't know anyone here. In New Orleans, I mean. I'm new in town. Would you...would you have lunch with me?"

There were about a million ways I could have done it better. Why had I said I was new in town, like I was reciting Eagles lyrics? Why not, "I've only been in town for a couple weeks, and I'm just getting to know the place"?

And obviously in New Orleans, moron.

Why hadn't I let what I was saying develop, by asking her if she knew anything in the neighborhood...and then I could ask her if she'd show me? And maybe ask her name first, dummy! It's probably not *actually* Mary Anne, jeez! And lunch, what the hell? I was eating lunch now.

Then I recalled something important: in every relationship I'd ever had, the other party has always said it didn't matter what you said.

What mattered was that you said something at all.

I looked at her, hope in my eyes, our future together hanging in the balance.

"Sorry. Can't. Boyfriend."

Inside my brain, my eyes clinched and I said, "DAMMIT!"

On the outside, in the real world, I said, "Oh, of course."

Then she made it worse.

She said, "But thanks for asking."

And smiled.

And my, oh my, was it a beautiful smile—one that sent my brain charging off again: *OK, people have boyfriends, but they also sometimes drop their boyfriends, so maybe, after I make the team, I'll turn this into my regular lunch place, but I'll never mention that I play for the Hornets, and she'll see me on TV when I have a good game against the Celtics or the Knicks and then she'll say, "Hey, you never said you played basketball," and I'll flash her a grin and tell her that she never asked, and then she'll loosen up, and the boyfriend will do something stupid, and then the whole thing will take shape just as I'd planned, but it'll be even better because of the funny origin story that is taking shape before my very eyes! All I have to do is make the team! This is going to happen!*

The Hornets cut me five days later, and one week after meeting the most beautiful waitress I'd ever seen, I was back in Kansas City, playing for the ABA's Knights and listening to the PA guy shoehorn that joke from *Airplane* every time I scored a basket.

"There's Paul 'Don't Call Me' Shirley for two!"

The day before I was let go by the Hornets, Coach Floyd told me my release was a shame. He hadn't realized I'd gotten as good as I'd gotten since college, and everyone in the organization knew I was better than the team's slow-footed draft pick. But the owner didn't want to look like a fool for having drafted the kid, so they were going to keep him around awhile. The good news, said Floyd, was that our plan had gone famously. I'd been better than advertised, and what that assistant had said about the player who played like me—well, he wasn't alone in that sentiment.

"Next summer," Coach Floyd said. "I wouldn't be surprised if we sign you to a contract."

I couldn't help but think about the waitress. Maybe she'd still be working at the same restaurant, maybe she'd remember me, maybe that boyfriend would be long gone, maybe we'd go on that date, maybe that would lead to her bedroom in the apartment with the exposed brick wall, maybe she'd take off her clothes and my clothes and-

The Hornets made the playoffs that year, where, as the Eastern Conference's fifth seed, they battled it out against the Miami Heat, losing in seven games—a respectable effort, especially for a team that had lost former All-Star Jamal Mashburn early in the season. Also, an effort that I thought would give my ol' college coach just the latitude he needed to add a hard-working ex-player of his own to the roster for the following season. Which is why I was so surprised to read online that the New Orleans Hornets had fired Floyd in favor of Byron Scott, who, the next season, would lead the Hornets to an 18-64 record.

A spot in the Hornets' lineup and a spot next to MARY ANNE in her feather bed: those things were always going to be figments, fantasies, things that would never be.

A lot like most plans, as it happens.

It is our habit as sentient beings to place ourselves into the future (or the past). It doesn't matter that this doesn't do us any good; we do it anyway.

I am no different, and I am probably worse. I can extrapolate, from one ten-second encounter or event, an entire future scenario.

Like, for example, the scenario that brings a black-haired former swimmer I met at an awards banquet in Phoenix to Russia,

where she falls hopelessly in love with me *and* my lifestyle, while also salving the loneliness that I'm feeling.

The real problem with this power is that it fails to take into account the feelings and desires of others. Like, for example, the feelings and desires of the black-haired former swimmer I met at an awards banquet in Phoenix, who had her own path: a path that would eventually lead her to a happy marriage in a Northeastern state.

And not to Russia.

Although, to be fair, if she had gone to Russia, she wouldn't have found me there.

LOS ANGELES

A Tuesday night

"Wait, wait, wait, you're telling me-"

She points a finger at my head, aiming it along the side of her drink. She leans in and pushes the flap of my ear into the ear canal, the way she has taught me tonight. I don't know why it works, but it does—mutes the excess noise somehow. The band we're watching is creating plenty of excess noise, which is probably why we're trying to talk and not just watching them.

"-you've never been drunk?"

I nod and smile, which is what I always do in this situation.

"How is that possible?" she mouths.

It is a fair question. It is also a question I've answered almost as many times as the height question, and so it is usually a question I want to answer about as much as I want to answer the height question. But something is different about this night, about this girl, and about this time in my life.

I nod toward the Troubadour's side bar, where there are pictures of Guns 'N Roses on the walls. I can't help but think of the first time I heard "Welcome to the Jungle." I was in the North Topeka Pizza Hut, and it was the scariest thing I'd ever heard. And now I'm here, in the same jungle Axl Rose was singing about, having said no to Russia and financial security, putting all my hopes behind Twentieth Century Fox and a television pilot we're calling *The 12th Man*.

When the girl can hear me, I explain my teetotaling to her. I tell her what I tell everyone, which is that it's because of basketball. But I also tell her what I don't tell everyone, which is that it's not entirely because of basketball. There's fear in there, too, and the feeling that if I've waited this long, why would I start now?

She looks at me.

"Do you trust me?"

I do trust her, and I want to trust her, and this is the nicest she's ever been, so I say yes.

It takes five beers.

When the show is over (she was right, music *is* better with booze) we go back to her apartment in Beverly Hills, which she shares with two girls that are her age and a cat that is not.

We're sitting on her bed when she asks:

"So, why me?"

5

The Second Time

My high school sexual exploits hit their not-so-proverbial climax when, senior year, my then-girlfriend took off her bra and began to grind on my crotch until I—if you'll pardon the use of an expression that was endemic to my small town—blew a load in the jeans I'd put on after the varsity basketball game that had finished an hour and a half before I did.

So I left high school a virgin. And needing new jeans.

Being a virgin as a freshman in college is like racing a car with the pedals switched: you know you can catch up if you figure out how this works, but catching up gets more and more difficult with each lap that goes by.

I went to Iowa State University to play basketball, and at Iowa State University, basketball was king. So the race shouldn't have been a race, and it bordered on inexcusable that, midwinter of freshman year, I was rolling around on the floor with a girl I'd asked out on the last day of Music 102 (because I was afraid to say anything before that), NOT taking off her pants.

I left freshman year a virgin, too.

This was taking on all the characteristics of "a problem."

A problem that was magnified by the cohorts with which I was spending most of my time: the men's basketball team. Some of the stories they told were downright terrifying: one of my teammates having sex with one girl while talking to another of my teammates on a cell phone about finding a different girl. Another leaving his room on the fourth floor of our dormitory in search of a condom on the fifth floor, while naked and with what I assumed, based on what I'd seen in the shower, must have been a spectacular erection.

In addition to being completely intimidated by first, sex and, second, the sex my teammates were having, I faced another obstacle: I'd been the least-heralded recruit on the team, which meant that I had very little room for on-court error. Also, I was trying for a degree in mechanical engineering. My life was a variation on the triangle women use to temper their expectations of men.

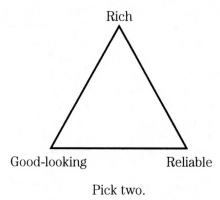

Rich

Good-looking   Reliable

Pick two.

My triangle looked like this:

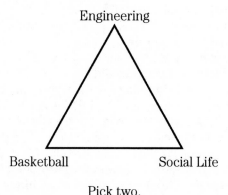

Engineering

Basketball   Social Life

Pick two.

So I didn't drink, I didn't go out, I didn't do much besides go to basketball practice, sleep, and study for the engineering classes that were treating my brain like they were the teeth in a wood-chipper, and my brain was the wood, and sophomore year almost got away from me, too. Sexually, I mean.

My second college basketball season ended in an uninspired loss to the University of Missouri at our conference tournament in Kansas City. From the perspective of Iowa State's endearingly dedicated fan base, it was the fitting end to what had been a dreadful year. Despite the addition of a freshman named Marcus Fizer, who on the heraldry spectrum fell on the exact opposite end of me, we'd won only 12 times in 30 tries, thus saddling Tim Floyd with his first losing season at Iowa State.

For me, though, the season had been something of a revelation. When Floyd periodically lost patience with Fizer's general petulance, he put me into the starting lineup, and, in the chaos that often envelopes sports teams' losing seasons, I'd proven myself to be a serviceable Division I basketball player, which would have come as a surprise to all the basketball coaches who'd thought, when I was in high school, that such would never be the case.

It seemed that my monk-like existence was paying off.

After the Missouri game, Floyd walked onto the bus that would take us back to our hotel in Kansas City, marched past my teammates, and stuck out his hand to shake mine.

"Good job, Paul," he said, his intense blue eyes drilling into mine.

I'd played well against Missouri, but I could tell that this handshake wasn't entirely about the game that had just finished. Floyd and I had developed an oddly intimate bond in the two years since he'd taken me on at Iowa State. One day after practice, he'd told me that he would have been OK with me dating his daughter—something, he said, that he'd only thought about one other player he'd coached: Fred Hoiberg, who would go on to follow in Floyd's footsteps by coaching the Cyclones of Iowa State *and* the Bulls of Chicago. I never dated Coach Floyd's daughter, of course, because *saying* you're OK with one of your players dating your daughter and actually *being* OK with one of your players dating your daughter are two very different things.

On the bus, I looked Floyd in the eye, told him thanks, and asked him if I could go home with my parents. Kansas City is markedly closer to Meriden, Kansas, than is Ames, Iowa, and all year—a year that had seen me miss my first Christmas (we'd been in Puerto Rico, where we'd lost to Texas Christian University by 49 points on Christmas Eve)—I'd looked forward with an inordinate amount of pleasure to the first time I'd get to go home.

In addition to being a virgin, I was also still prone to the homesickness that had haunted me since Science Camp. These factoids being, most likely, quite related.

"Of course," he said, simultaneously smiling and squinting like an actor in a Western before turning to return to the front of the bus. Two months later, he accepted that offer to become the next head coach of the Chicago Bulls.

I spent the next three days at home glorying in my newfound freedom. For the first time in eight months, no one was screaming at me, I wasn't being made to run line drills, and I could go to sleep without worrying about how I was going to defend Marcus Fizer, who might have been a year younger than I was but was about three times better at basketball.

While I was home, a rogue springtime winter storm blanketed most of the Midwest in wet snow. This was no great bother to me; after a winter in Ames, whose climate is more like Poland's than people realize, I'd grown used to the cold and snow. Except for one problem: I had a chemistry test on Monday and I had to get back to school. I'd planned on an airborne return to Iowa, but every flight from Kansas City to Des Moines had been cancelled. So my father drove me through the snow to the downtown Kansas City Greyhound station, which was appropriately redolent of Colt .45, both pre- and post-human filtration, and we secured for me a ticket on the northbound bus.

Then, just as I was saying goodbye to him, someone grabbed my shoulder and said, "Are you going to Ames?"

I turned to find that the voice had come from a female person who stood 5'9" and had brown eyes that made me think of those Arabian tents that are filled with thick rugs and smell like incense.

"Uh, yeah," I said.

She smiled.

"Good. Me, too."

My dad winked at me as he left, because that's what dads do when their virginal sons are about to get stuck on five-hour bus rides with pretty girls. I got onto the bus and sat down in an aisle seat, glaring at everyone who approached so they wouldn't sit in the seat across the aisle from me. Until the girl with the eyes out of the Ottoman Empire got on, of course.

"Is this one taken?" she asked, nodding toward the seat across the aisle from me. I'd like to think I shook my head and gestured idly at the vacant seat, or maybe that I said, "Only by you."

But what actually happened was closer to, "Urgle gurgle, um, no."

And so began an impromptu, eight-hour date with Shelly McQuaid, who was coming home to Ames for the final rotation of her training as a physical therapist. Her flight from Philadelphia had been diverted to Kansas City thanks to the snow, and the only way she could get to Ames was the bus, just like me. At each stop in our trip north—in Cameron, Eagleville, Lamoni—Shelly and I got out and wandered the aisles of whatever gas station was near the stop. Then, back to the bus and our slow ride through the Midwestern darkness. The snow only got thicker as we progressed north; there were times when our bus was the lone vehicle on the highway, which only further contributed to the deepening night's Apocalyptic feel.

Shelly had left Ames for college back East, where she'd played volleyball for a program that was among the nation's best. After college, she'd spent two years playing professionally in the sand. Then she'd gotten serious about the rest of her life and had started training as a physical therapist. By the time we arrived at the Ames Greyhound station at 1 a.m., three hours later than our scheduled arrival time, I'd also learned that Shelly had seen the rock band Live long before they'd hit it big with their seminal album *Throwing Copper*, that she'd once been engaged to a professional baseball player, that she was 26, and that, like me, she had no idea how she was going to get home from the bus station in Ames.

I told Shelly that if we could just get to campus, I could get her home from there. She asked someone who had more dedicated friends than we did if we could hitch a ride, which is how we found ourselves in the back of a banged-up Jeep Cherokee, huddled like two kids on the way to the lake, en route to the dorm parking lot, where the Chevrolet Corsica my parents had helped me buy just prior to my senior year of high school was—no surprise—buried in snow. After I dusted it off with the oversized scraper I'd bought at the start of Iowa's winter in late August, I was left with one last obstacle before I could squire Shelly to her parents' house: behind my car was a two-foot snow ridge left by whichever sadist had plowed the dorm parking lot. Shelly cheered as I, using a skill I'd seen my father deploy with far more aplomb than I was capable of, rocked the car back and forth, Drive, Reverse, Drive, Reverse, Drive, Reverse, until YES, I was out.

I drove Shelly down Lincoln Way and up a hill, then left and past Campustown, an area of Ames frequented for the purposes of inebriation and flirtation by normal college students (read: not me). Guided by the sodium vapor reflected in the snow on the McQuaid yard, I parked on the street, turned off the Corsica, and helped Shelly and her bags to the door of her parents' house. There, with both of us consumed by partial disbelief that we'd survived the icy ride up I-35, I did what came natural to me, which was to say, "OK, well, it was nice to meet you," and drive away without getting her number, email address, or any other way to contact her.

The next day, I woke up angry for two reasons:

1. The chemistry test I'd thought was on Monday was actually on Tuesday.

2. I'd blown it with a girl who seemed to like me, who was sophisticated, witty, very pretty, and who also—did I mention this—WAS A FORMER PROFESSIONAL VOLLEYBALL PLAYER.

I did have one checkmark in my Clue notebook. Shelly had explained to me where she would be working while in Ames: the physical therapy clinic inside the Lied Recreational Center, not a quarter mile from my dorm room. So, after Tuesday's chemistry test, I hiked through the still-Decembery Iowa air to the rec

center, where I stood outside the door to the physical therapy department for ten minutes, rehearsing what I would say between time-killing trips to every drinking fountain in the building.
Then I strode stumbled inside and asked the receptionist if Shelly McQuaid was around.

"Hi," she said with a smile, holding a manila envelope as she walked out of an exam room. "I wasn't sure I'd ever see you again."

I blushed, recovered, launched in.

"Well, hey, so I know you're new in town or, well, not new, I guess, but you haven't been here in a while and so I was thinking, or I thought, maybe, if you want, we could, I don't know, go to a movie or something sometime?"

Shelly looked at me, patting the envelope against her hand while I held my breath, terrified that I'd made a colossal miscalculation, and in front of the entire office. Then she said, "I'd love that," before taking a yellow brochure from the envelope and writing her phone number on it. It's one of four telephone numbers I can still remember, in part because I hung it on the bulletin board in my dorm room and in part because, besides me, no one without Asperger's remembers phone numbers anymore.

But mostly because it was the phone number of the first girl I ever loved.

Our first date was, in fact, a movie—something forgettable in the theater in Campustown. Afterward, we had Blizzards at Dairy Queen and I accidentally called her the wrong name and she was miffed, but the truth was I was just nervous. Our first kiss happened in her parents' driveway, in the same spot where I'd failed to ask for her number the week before. Afterward, still giddy from the thrill of the kiss, which had been far different from my previous Greatest Hits (the furtive efforts I'd mustered in high school and with the girl from Music 102) I backed out of her parents' driveway and directly into a car across the street.

I cursed and punched the steering wheel. Then I calmed myself; in reality I'd only tapped the car behind me. I got out to check the damage.

It didn't look like a tap. I'd crushed the driver's side door on a white Buick Regal built around the time Oliver North was in the news.

I got back in the car and pulled into the McQuaid driveway to face what I'd done.

Before I got to the door, Shelly burst through, laughing inside the halo cast by her parents' porch light. I looked over my shoulder and put my hands in the pockets of the blue L.L. Bean parka my parents had equipped me with before I left for the Arctic Northern Midwest.

"I'm sorry," she said, wiping those brown eyes of hers. "It's not funny. It's just, I saw the whole thing, so I could see you in the street, deciding what to do."

I could feel my face twisting into embarrassment. Here was this pretty, *experienced* girl who'd just kissed me and who seemed to like me, and I'd gone and screwed it up, like a little kid.

Shelly grabbed my hand, her eyes hitting all the corners of mine.

"Don't worry, it was already like that. My dad smashed it like five years ago. That car's a running joke with the neighborhood."

The giddy feeling was back.

"So we don't have to call the cops?"

"No, silly."

"Whew."

"You're awfully cute," she said. And she kissed me again.

As one might imagine, this was all pretty heady stuff for a twenty-year-old virgin. It was to get only headier when, four dates later, and after the Tonic concert inside Hilton Coliseum, part of the VEISHEA celebration that Iowa State used to hold each spring, before people started getting stabbed and killed.

(Yes, stabbed and killed in Iowa. And yes, Tonic, the rock band.)

During a break between songs, Shelly leaned into me and whispered, "Do you want to get laid?"

As we approached my dorm room and its solid wood door, unadorned by the sorts of dry-erase paraphernalia that some of our dorm-mates had on their doors, I didn't know whether I wanted my roommate of two years, a Mississippian and fellow basketball player, to be home or not. I wanted to have sex with the same burning desire of any guy with a pretty girl who he likes a lot on his arm. But I also did not want to embarrass myself, which seemed a likely outcome of this event, in the same way that a dip into the ocean would be a likely outcome if the Air Force put a blind man in charge of landing a plane on an aircraft carrier.

I tried the door with a sheepish/terrified glance at Shelly. It didn't turn. My roommate was gone. This sex thing was going to happen. Inside my room, Shelly turned off the lights, and then we got out of our clothes, tossing them into oddly neat piles at the end of my bed, right next to the pole that held the set of shelves my father had helped me build before freshman year. Then, after approximately two minutes, a cold sweat washed across my body and I sat up on the bed.

"Um, you need to know something about me," I said, staring at the darkened 19-inch TV I'd bought with the per diem I'd saved over Christmas break my freshman year. I half-wished I was watching that TV with my roommate, No-Girls-Allowed-style.

"I already do," she said.

My eyes whirled to Shelly, who was, by now, completely naked, and who looked positively enticing in that state.

"You do?"

"Of course!"

"Are we talking about the same thing?"

She slapped my thigh.

"Yeah! You only do anal. You silly athletes."

"What? That's not-"

She laughed.

"I know, dummy," she said. "You want to tell me you've never done this before."

I felt my shoulders slump.

"Yeah. Is that a problem?"

Shelly pushed off her back and folded herself around me. I could feel one of her breasts on my shoulder.

"I just told you, I know. And I knew when we came here. Now the question is: do you want me to be your first?"

I looked back at her. Then I nodded downward, where my penis, heretofore only a participant in the act of urination, was reawakening.

She laughed again, putting her hand in my naked lap: the first time even *that* had happened. We were breaking a lot of ground.

"Good," she said. "But there is one thing you need to know about me."

I was losing cognitive function, which made my voice lower and slower and probably a little creepy. I said, "Yeah?" as I kissed her.

"Yeah. I only have sex with people I'm in love with, and who are in love with me."

Each day when I woke up, my first thought was of what I needed to tell Shelly. When I went to sleep, my last thought was what I'd forgotten to say. I was only 20, and I'd never had sex, but that seemed like love to me.

So I told Shelly McQuaid that I loved her, and she told me the same. And then, after a few of the fits and starts that are applicable to everyone not in the Rolling Stones, Shelly and I did the sex thing I'd heard so much about.

Because it was Shelly, it seemed like I was in competent hands (and other body parts, CYMBAL CRASH), what with her being 30% older than I was. This hunch—about Shelly's ability to create a nurturing environment for one's first sexual experience—was confirmed when she said, "Are you sure you've never done this before?"

Which was the right thing to say, even if there was no way it was sincere. I hadn't crashed my plane into the ocean, but I'd definitely scared some people in the tower.

When it was over, and when she was gone, back to her parents' house, and after I'd slept the best sleep in my two decades on Earth, I woke up and thought, "I will now go downstairs to breakfast as a Person Who's Had Sex. I wonder if everyone will be able to tell the difference."

They couldn't, of course. But something was different, yeah, something was new, something was...

Holy shit! I was going to have to do this again, wasn't I?

I will grant you that the reaction I had is not the standard reaction of a normal red-blooded American male. But I am not a normal red-blooded American male. One of the many, many things I'd taken from that first sexual encounter was that there were a lot of things that could go wrong. The condom, for one: I mean, I know I was supposed to be an expert, what with a Sex Ed.-teaching mom, but goodness gracious there were a lot of ins and outs (ahem!) to the process, especially with her watching and, I mean, seriously, she's 26, she's got, like a, 700 to one lead on me here...

"Hey!"

(While I was worrying, she had called on the dorm phone my roommate and I shared.)

"Hi!"

"So, when are we going to do that again?"

Oh jeez, we're not even going to pretend that it might not happen? This is a guarantee? This is something that's going into the daily planner? Oh shit, oh shit, oh shit.

"Um, well, how about Tuesday? I mean, I have to go to Campus Health to get my end-of-season physical after class, but maybe after that?"

"That would be perfect," she said.

After class on Tuesday, I went to my exit physical at the Campus Health Building with nothing but sex on my mind, which explains why, after measuring my blood pressure once, the nurse called over the team doctor, a balding man cursed to look perpetually like he was hiding a throw pillow under his shirt.

He wrapped the cuff on my arm, pumped it again, and listened to the blood coursing through the vessels in my arm.

"One sixty over ninety-seven," he said with a glance at my eyes. "That's a little elevated, Paul. Is your blood pressure normally that high?"

"Uh," I said. "Maybe I'm a little stressed about finals?"

I wasn't stressed about finals, of course. I was stressed about The Sex. I was also stressed about the fact that I was stressed about The Sex, wondering a thing that I would wonder many more times in my life: what if I can't stop worrying about this?

The team doctor accepted my explanation without a second thought. The purpose of an end-of-season exit physical is to confirm that the recipient isn't going to sue anyone if he falls ill over the summer, not to spelunk the inner workings of that recipient's overactive worry centers.

The post-physical sex went off without catastrophe, probably because at age 20, anxiety is no match for hormones, and Shelly and I were together for the next two months. Inseparable, more or less. She didn't know anyone else in Ames; most of her high school classmates were gone. And I'd never been in love before. Plus, basketball was done for the year; my choice line on the triangle had shifted.

So, accompanied by a pretty girl WHO I WAS BONING, I went to Iowa State baseball games and we hit golf balls in the back of the Maple-Willow-Larch dormitory complex and we went to more movies in Campustown and we had sex as often as we could, which wasn't all that often because I could only talk my roommate into letting me have our room so many times.

Then the school year ended and I had to go back to my parents' house in Kansas, and Shelly had to go back to Pennsylvania. I assumed we'd stay in touch and figure out how it would work out. We were in love, and that's what people who were in love did. Right?

Shelly had different ideas. After she went back East, I couldn't get her to return my calls. A package I put together, which included a copy of the *City of Angels* soundtrack and one of my Iowa State jerseys (I imagined her wearing it while she slept) got no response. Yet still I carried the torch. All through the summer, and into the next fall. Shelly came home to Ames for Thanksgiving, and I went to see her at her parents' house—same porch, same driveway, same Buick across the street. I asked her if she wanted to come to the apartment I'd rented with my best friend.

She shook her head.

"Paul, look-"

Then she explained that it was over, had been over, that we both had lives we had to pursue.

This time, as I was backing out of the McQuaid driveway, I almost couldn't see the Buick Regal I knew was behind me. My first love was done, over, kaput, and the tears rolling down my cheeks were a pretty good indication of how I felt, which was that I couldn't imagine how or when I'd recover from the heartbreak I'd just endured.

It was another year before I felt even like kissing anyone else. During that year, I resolved that I'd never let myself fall so hard again; I couldn't think of what good might possibly have come out of my short-lived relationship with Shelly McQuaid. But that was just the narrow view of a lovesick male in his early twenties. Because once the fog cleared, I figured out that I'd been given a gift, while also ducking a *Super Mario*-sized bullet.

Shelly had given me the best introduction to sex and love a person can get. Even though I am male and males are supposed to not care about sex—are supposed to be able to distance themselves from their feelings so they can GET IT ON whenever and wherever that GETTING IT ON is most convenient and most available—the sex I'd had with Shelly was going to serve as a pretty good model of what I should look for in a relationship from now on. Sure, it had been a short-lived affair, and sure, I'd been in awe most of the time we'd been together. But those circumstances had led to something that had to have been better than some frantic coupling in the back seat of a rusty truck somewhere in Jefferson County.

Second, and maybe more important, Shelly had done me the great favor of letting me go. I couldn't imagine it at the time because I was a heartsick 20-year-old, but there was, of course, no way my first love affair was going to last. Nor should it have. I needed to go out into the world, and I needed to meet other people, and I needed to learn what that first love meant, in the context of a lot of other loves. I needed to meet people like-

"Me?"

I smile across the bed, trying to echo the smile I dished out at the Troubadour earlier. And probably failing. I was sober then. I'm not now.

"Yeah," I say, because it's the truth. Then I start laughing. Something has just occurred to me.

She slaps me on the shoulder.

"What?" she says.

"There's one thing I left out," I say.

She spins her fingers, telling me to get on with it.

I sit up and lean against the wall her bed is smashed against. I take a deep breath.

"Shelly was—is, I suppose—Jewish."

"What."

She says it like that, no question mark.

"So, what," she says. "You just go through life getting guidance from Jewish girls?"

Because, you see, this girl whose room I'm in: she's Jewish, too.

"Maybe?" I say. "What's weird, though, is that when I met Shelly, I didn't even know the difference between a Jew and, like, a Presbyterian."

"Oh, you're so tolerant," she says.

"I'm serious! I kind of think you all make a bigger deal out of it than we do. I mean, she was the one who said her family would never be OK with her ending up with a Gentile like me. Meanwhile, I had no reason to think anything of it."

For a moment, she is silent. Then she says, "Yeah, I don't know if my family would be thrilled, either."

"See?!"

She smacks me with a pillow.

"So anyway, you never answered my question. Why me?"

"The story was its own answer."

"Spell it out for me."

I groan and slump against the wall.

"Well, it's just like it was with Shelly, I guess. Timing is everything, right? This is the right time and place for me to finally let down my guard and get drunk, and you're the right person for me to let down my guard with."

She seems satisfied with this answer, and so I lean in to kiss her, which is a thing I know to do only because Shelly McQuaid taught me.

But she stops me.

"Just don't let down your guard too far. I'm fine with being responsible for your initiation into the world of drinking. I'm not sure I want to be responsible for your heart, too."

I'm not listening when she says this. But I should be.

LAS VEGAS

A Saturday Night

A man who looks like Ving Rhames is holding out his fist for a bump. Actually, it might *be* Ving Rhames, for all I know. Teri Hatcher is one row ahead of us.

The man who looks like Ving Rhames: he's a couple rows behind us, and his arm is reaching through an entire row to get to me.

"Congrats," he says with a solemn smile.

I bump his fist and turn back to Scott.

"Again?" he asks.

"Yup," I say, nodding and staring straight ahead, at a stage where Sting should be coming on at any moment.

"Even worse today, probably. Draft was this weekend."

I chuckle at this, but I keep my face aimed at the stage. I don't need to give away the truth. The poor guy is probably excited. He thinks he's just met former USC quarterback Matt Leinart, the newest member of the NFL's Arizona Cardinals.

Leinart and I are both tall and white and we have the same hair and the same scruffy, hipster-approved beard. So I get it. Especially here, relatively close to the stage at a Tiger Woods-sponsored charity event, in a time when Tiger Woods isn't yet a known philanderer. This seems like the sort of place where Matt Leinart might be.

"You ready?" Scott asks.

The lights have just gone down. Sting is about to take the stage.

I don't particularly care about Sting, but I'm happy to humor Scott, who thinks this is going to be great.

"Sure," I say, and Sting grabs the microphone.

The next two hours are pleasant enough. Sting might not be my bag, but he does take my mind off the state of my life, which is a confusing state indeed.

The girl who got me drunk for the first time: she wasn't kidding about not letting my guard down too much. On New Year's Eve, I rushed to a party to meet her after getting home from Seattle, where the exiled Chinese basketball team I was playing for had played two games in three days.

When I arrived at the party, she seemed happy to see me; we spent the evening draped across one another in a chair before spending the night draped across one another in that bed in her apartment.

But when we woke up the next morning, she rolled over and said, "I think we should just be friends."

And that, well…it wasn't a surprise, exactly. There'd been plenty of signs, like what she'd said that night she'd gotten me drunk, and what she'd said about how her parents would probably never be OK with me, and what she'd said about how she wasn't sure what she wanted from me, or from life.

However, just because it wasn't exactly a surprise didn't mean it didn't hurt, especially with it being New Year's and all.

I spent the next month trying to win her back, a task that was complicated by the other two rails in my life: the Chinese basketball team and the television pilot.

The former had come into my life because I'd been looking to hedge my bets when I moved to Los Angeles. Twentieth Century Fox had given us the go-ahead to *write* the pilot based on my idea, but that didn't mean we were going to get to *make* the pilot. So I'd begun casting about for a minor league basketball team that might be excited to have a player who'd spent part of each of the past three seasons playing in the NBA.

Through an old teammate, I heard about a Chinese basketball team that was playing in the ragtag minor league called the ABA. The team had been kicked out of the top Chinese league because its owner had refused to sell its best player to one of the best two teams in the league. Or so the story went. Whatever the truth was, the team wanted a couple of Americans to serve as mentors when their players needed mentors and to serve as stopgaps when they needed a basket.

At first, the arrangement had been ideal. I was allowed to do whatever I wanted on the court, we practiced only once a day, and I was keeping my hat in the ring, in the off chance an NBA team needed someone for a short-term contract. But then things started to go sideways, as things will do when you're playing for an exiled Chinese basketball team that has put down shallow roots in Los Angeles.

Our games were on television back in China. I thought this was true because the team had a passionate fan base back in the Motherland, but I learned that the cameras were in place mostly so our eccentric owner could watch the games. But even that seemed acceptable until he started making substitutions from his bedroom.

The procedure went as follows: he watched the games while connected via cellular phone to a woman who sat in the stands at all our games. If the owner saw something he didn't like, he'd tell the woman to make a change. She'd walk down to the bench, tap a Chinese player on the shoulder, and the player would walk past our hapless American coach and check himself into the game.

When I first sniffed out what was going on, I was mildly amused. How pleasantly absurd!

Until, of course, it started affecting me. I would go in for 45 seconds at a time and get pulled after making a basket, or because the owner's feet itched under his blankets in China, I never could tell.

So, after a "home" game (we played in a recreation center in East Los Angeles), I folded up my jersey and handed it to the team manager.

In my game of Life, basketball was banished to the back seat of my tiny plastic car.

My decision had been made easier by the good news we were getting about our television pilot. Fox had commissioned us to film it, under one condition: I had to learn how to act. The executives at Fox weren't sure we were going to be able to find someone to play the lead, as the lead needed to look like a basketball player, and Los Angeles isn't filled with actors who also look like basketball players.

And so, my life has taken on a routine I never would have predicted. Every day, I report to the Fox lot in Century City to meet with my new acting coach, a tiny fireball with a history of turning non-actors into passable ones. We bounce around the top floor of an abandoned sound stage, with her reminding me to "just be a kid!" and me slowly evolving into someone who might be good enough at acting to play...himself.

Then, when I'm done for the day, I go home to my apartment, which is next door to Scott's apartment, and we figure out what we're going to do that night.

I met Scott in training camp with the Lakers, when I was fresh out of college and had short Republican hair. We didn't talk much that time around, partly because I was fixated on basketball and partly because I could tell Scott was much cooler than I was. He was a mountain of a human, dwarfing everyone in camp except Shaquille O'Neal, with an easy charm that verged on being too easy.

We lost contact when the Lakers sent me home. But then, after the Jewish girl broke up with me, I realized I was going to need some friends. So I called Scott, and he showed me what going out was really like, just like he's about to do now because Sting is done, and we're about to hit the afterparty.

"What'd you think?" Scott asks as we navigate toward the House of Blues that is inside this casino.

"I kept thinking he should be able to hold his notes longer," I say.

Scott looks at me, his brow wrinkly.

"You know, because of the Tantric thing?"

Scott laughs, a guffaw that sounds like something a Medieval king would produce. He curls one of his giant mitts around my shoulders and I follow him inside.

This feeling, I have to admit, is a nice one. For once, I've not had to be the trailblazer, the coordinator, the big brother. I've allowed Scott to take over, when it comes to plans and lines and doormen. He *knows* people and he can almost always talk his way into a party.

Speaking of parties, this one isn't great, so it isn't long before we're out on the casino floor amongst the chain-smoking proletariat. Scott isn't thrilled by this turn of events. He's great with known obstacles, but less great with chaos. He also doesn't like doing "normal" things. Witness our setup here: the friend who invited us is a cofounder of some video game company. He paid for each of us to have our own suite in the Bellagio. He sent a Maybach to take us to the Sting concert.

Then, up by a craps table that is only half-heartedly surrounded by gamblers, a prospect that might solve all our problems: two teachers from Idaho, having a "girls weekend." They're dressed exactly like two teachers from Idaho should dress on a girls' weekend: conservative blouses unbuttoned by exactly two more buttons than in class.

While we're talking to them, I look to Scott and watch him calculate. He looks like a lion deciding whether this is the time to strike.

"So, girls, want to join us at the party?"

He has decided that it is.

We walk back to the House of Blues. Scott is confident, I know, that we'll be able to get in. We've got the lanyards that allow us access, and it's never hard to get pretty girls into a party.

Scott bounds up the steps to the doorman in front of the velvet rope, leaving me to talk to the girls. They are refreshingly kindhearted, but I can already tell they're watching Scott. As Craig Finn from The Hold Steady sings, "Guys go for looks, girls go for status."

Scott is in conference with the burly doorman for longer than I expect, so I make the girls laugh, or try to. Such is the lot of the Beta male—the role I am shoehorned into whenever Scott is around.

There's a commotion at the top of the small set of stairs. It's Scott, waving the doorman off. He slinks down the steps in a way that tells the story before he does.

"Dude says no pass, no entry."

The girls are deflated. They thought they were going to a hot party with a couple of happenin' fellas. Now they're just standing in the casino, like every other pair of teachers from Idaho.

We are just as deflated. We've pushed our chips into the middle with these two, and we already know the party isn't exactly Studio 54. At least, if we had them, we could make fun of it being dull together.

Then, from behind the velvet rope, a particular black man appears with the suddenness of the genie he once dressed as.

It's MC Hammer.

And he's yelling at the doorman.

"Yo, what are you thinking? He can bring whoever he wants in here!"

Then MC Hammer points at me and it hits me like the cannonball in the fat man's belly.

MC Hammer thinks I am Matt Leinart.

I glance at Scott and say everything without saying anything. He gives me an almost imperceptible nod. I grab the hand of the nearest teacher from Idaho, who has suddenly gotten her glow back. Scott puts his arm around the other teacher from

Idaho, who is just as glowy, and we mount the steps like it's the end of *Return of the Jedi*.

When we reach the top, I nod at the doorman, forgiving him for a crime he didn't commit. Then Scott pulls the two girls into the party, leaving me standing in front of MC Hammer.

I have concerns.

Like, have "we" met before? Is he going to ask me to sign something? Is he about to realize that there's no way a quarterback would be 6'9"?

"You good?" he asks. He's drinking something red. Maybe vodka and cranberry. Maybe just cranberry.

"Yeah," I say.

"Cool," he says. He holds out a fist for me to bump. "You need anything, you let me know, K?"

I bump his fist and nod, because I think that's what Matt Leinart would do. And then I scurry into the party after Scott and the teachers.

When I arrive, everything has changed. For once, I am the one who got us into the party. Never mind that it had nothing to do with me.

Scott grins.

"So, Matty, how's that offense looking?"

The girls are thoroughly confused. Scott offers to get drinks. I ask for a beer. He ducks into the crowd.

The girls turn to me and one of them asks, "What just happened?"

With a smile, I explain the mix-up.

When I am done, the other one says, "That's pretty quick thinking on your part."

"I don't know about that," I say. "I think I was just trying to make an old boss proud."

The looks on their faces tell me I should explain.

6

First Job, Worst Job

When Jim Reese, the baldheaded proprietor of Skinner's Nursery and Garden Store, first asked me if I was looking for a weekend job that might turn into a summer job, I responded just like my parents had taught me whenever I didn't really want to do something: I said I'd think about it.

I was poor, but I was 16. My Saturday nights were not occupied by beer bashes at the lake. They were spent fighting with my father and brothers about whether we would watch *Saturday Night Live*, *American Gladiators*, or *Star Trek: The Next Generation*. (It was a marvelous era for late night television.)

In other words: I wasn't finding my poverty particularly alarming.

That is, until a crisp spring day in Meriden when I asked Kelly Stepka if she'd come outside with me. After we were finished eating lunch, of course.

It's getting nice, so it makes sense to go outside. Here, I would like to open this door for you.

These are all things I said out loud.

In front of the high school, with the flag's rope banging against the pole every four seconds, Kelly must have been able to see what was coming like she was a highway worker and I was a big-rig driver barreling down the interstate at her with four shots of Five-Hour Energy in his stomach. But to her credit, she played along, saying nothing as I fidgeted, staring at the concrete for too long before finally looking her in her glasses-clad blue eyes and saying, "Um, so, I was just wondering...let's say, that, you know, like, if I asked you on a date, would you say yes?"

We'd been doing a lot of SAT prep, so the analogy that came to mind for how I felt while I awaited her answer was:

my heart : my throat :: a goose : a garden hose

Kelly pushed her bangs out of her eyes and smiled in the way girls can do to let you know that even though you're an idiot of the highest order, they're letting you off with a slap on the wrist.

"I would say I would be delighted," she said.

The goose dissolved into a warm, contented, terrified feeling in my stomach. I was going on a date!

That night, as I lay in bed, I conjured an image of Kelly's strawberry-blonde hair and how it had that poof in front, like every girl had in 1994.

Kelly had had me vexed for months. This was her thing; she was a serial vexer. One month it was Max Phalen. The next, Darin Densmore. Now it was my turn, as evidenced by the tiny notes we exchanged in Geometry class—the precursor to texting. Sometimes, the precursor to sexting. She tossed them over her shoulder onto my desk when the teacher was at the board. I read them, wrote my response on the back, and tossed them into her lap. I had a collection of them in my sock drawer.

I imagined what it would be like, if Kelly were to pick me as hers, how that would feel. Then I went past imagination: I made it a reality. Kelly would be my girlfriend soon. We'd start hanging around at each other's houses and going to things together and-

Wait, this could get expensive! And I didn't have any money!

The next day, I called Jim Reese and asked if the job was still available.

He said it was.

I told him I was in.

He told me to come to work on Sunday.

On Saturday, I picked up Kelly at two in the afternoon. When we got to my house, I challenged her to a game of one-on-one on the concrete slab that my brothers and I had helped my

father install three years before. Kelly had spent the season as the starting point guard on the varsity basketball team, so it was logical, I thought, to involve as much basketball as I could. During our game, which I engineered as both a win and a loss for me (no blocking shots, copious post-ups for the sake of body contact), I sweated through the T-shirt I'd picked out specifically for this event, a new one my mother let me get at JC Penney. Its back said something about fear and not having it: a philosophy I desperately wanted to make my own.

After I changed into my back-up outfit (likely something made by JC Penney's store brand, Arizona Jeans Co.), I joined Kelly in front of the television and we watched the University of Kansas win a basketball game. At halftime, Kelly lay down on her stomach on the floor in front of me, her jean shorts riding up when she plopped down, and I visualized a day when I might be able to act on the impulses that flashed like lightning through my brain every time I saw the faint tan lines in front of me. Which wasn't then, obviously. I mean, it's not like I had the house to myself or anything. (I absolutely, positively had the house to myself.)

After the game, Kelly and I went into the kitchen to look at the day's *Topeka Capital-Journal* to check the listings, and I acted like I hadn't long since pored over our options, and like I didn't know that we only had one, really, because A) we were only 16 and B) it was the spring. Summertime would've been easier; we wouldn't have had to watch *Guarding Tess* starring Nicholas Cage and my inadvertent namesake, Shirley MacLaine.

Then, a drink of water and the walk downstairs after I checked to make sure the sliding door was shut and the dogs were inside. Next up, the passenger door, because that's what a gentleman does, and then, as I walked from her door to mine, a sigh of relief.

So far, my plans had gone swimmingly. Basketball *in vivo* had kept us focused on a common activity, and basketball *eminus* had kept us focused on a common activity, and a movie would surely keep us focused on a yet another common activity.

We just had to get through the drive to the theater. No reason to worry about that, though. Because I had a plan for that, too.

I started the station wagon I was only allowed to borrow on special occasions, and we rode up the back driveway at my parents' house, past the apricot tree, and left onto a gravel road that would one day be labeled 43rd Street but back then was just the one that ran along the north side of our property. I waited for the next left onto Detlor Road, and I began thinking back to the list I'd made up the day before: three questions I could ask. I'd even written them down, in the haphazard cursive I would employ until an engineering teacher taught me in college how to write in block letters.

"So, what's your favorite movie?"

Relevant, I'd thought, when putting together the list. We were, in fact, driving to a movie.

"Hmmm," Kelly said. Or intoned. Or something meant to indicate that she wasn't all that interested in my line of questioning. "I don't really think I have one; it's so hard to pick, especially when you consider that there are all sorts of movies—comedies and dramas—and it's really hard to compare them, don't you think?"

Kelly, if I thought that, I wouldn't have asked the question. But thank you for preparing me for the sort of bullshit answer that dull girls will give to that question for the upcoming two decades.

The real problem, though, was that Question One hadn't even gotten us to K-4. We weren't even out of the gravel. But *No Fear!* They call it a "list" for a reason.

"So, what do you think you'll do after high school?"

"Probably go to KU."

Wait, I didn't mean, "What are you going to do for the four years immediately following high school?" I meant, "What are you going to do within the totality of your life? Your hopes, your dreams, your ambitions? Fill the air with your zany plans and wacky goals. Tell me everything!"

Or, answer this crafty follow-up question, which I just came up with:

"But, like, after that?"

"I don't know, it's a long way off."

The good news was that we'd made it to Highway 24, so we had only ten miles to go to the West Ridge 6 Theater. The bad news: I only had one question left. I'd really thought these questions would inspire longer answers.

"Have you ever thought about who would come to your funeral?"

Her mouth twitched almost imperceptibly.

"What do you mean?"

"I don't know. Like, do you ever think about who would come, or who you would want to come?"

And by this, I wanted to broach—in a sixteen-year-old's way—what it means to leave a legacy. Does it matter, really, what we do, or what people will think of us when we're gone, if we can't actually see who comes to our funerals? I wanted Kelly to imagine we could. Just for a little while, just to see where it took us.

She crossed her arms. "I don't like to think about things like that."

We rode the rest of the way to Topeka in an awkward, somewhat macabre silence.

Guarding Tess was mostly awful, but it did give us something to talk about on our walk through West Ridge Mall's parking lot, en route to the station wagon. Then, for the trip home, quiet again. I told myself that silence was OK; I had on my side darkness and fatigue and the safest radio station I could think of: Magic 108, "Playing all your favorites from the 60s, 70s and 80s."

At Kelly's house, she reached across the seat and hugged me. I made no moves, no efforts at a first kiss. The crush of her chest against mine was plenty—a promise of things to come, on later dates. And anyway, I had to go to work in the morning.

Skinner's Nursery and Garden Store was exactly 14 minutes from my parents' house, assuming you didn't get caught by either of the stoplights on the way. On my first day, I cruised through those intersections in the same station wagon, the radio dial on 105.9, the college alt-rock station I actually liked. Alice In Chains had just released the album with the three-legged dog on it. "Today" by Smashing Pumpkins was, I was pretty sure, the best song I'd ever heard.

I parked the car in the grass in back of the customer parking lot and went inside, where Jim Reese explained my duties: I was in charge of assisting customers to their cars with whatever purchases they'd just made. I smiled at old ladies and joked with cashiers, and my six-hour day slipped by like a buckskin canoe in a gurgling creek.

At the end of the afternoon, standing next to a display case filled with every variety of flower and vegetable seed I'd ever imagined, Jim held out his hand and I shook it and he said he'd see me next Sunday. I got into the station wagon and turned on the radio, tired but satisfied. I'd survived my first day of work *and* I'd made something like $25—plenty of money for another date.

All I had to do was ask Kelly.

But asking Kelly turned out to be trickier than I expected. For some reason, I didn't run into her at school as often that next week. But no matter, I thought, this would just give me a chance to save up a little more money. I went to work again the next Sunday, folded my boxes, helped my old ladies, shook Jim's hand, got back into the station wagon. The drive home didn't feel quite as good, but I knew what the problem was: I needed that second date; I needed to get serious about KS + PS.

That week, I found Kelly between classes and asked if she wanted to go out again. She looked at me, her head tilting as her eyes narrowed.

"I don't know," she said.

"OK!" I said. "Let me know when you decide."

As anyone with a vague understanding of human behavior could predict, Kelly had already decided. It took me a little longer to get the message. Like, about the time Kelly stopped sitting in front of me in Geometry, thus destroying our line of communication: her right shoulder, over which we'd tossed the notes we were writing on inch-long scraps of notebook paper. The end of the notes meant no more fantasies about back rubs in hot tubs, no more jokes about our teacher's Lego hair, no more requests for phone calls, and it was official: Kelly had moved on to vexing other members of my class.

I'd never been close to having a girlfriend—a realization that hit me like a kick from a cartoon kangaroo one night in bed, a few days after Kelly switched seats in Geometry. I turned off the light in my basement bedroom and curled around a belly that was filled with inexplicable spasms as I sobbed myself to sleep.

But rejection at the hands of Kelly Stepka did not absolve me of my handshake commitment to working at Skinner's. I'd agreed to an entire summer of employment, three days a week: two eight-hour weekdays, and one six-hour Sunday.

Jim Reese had on his payroll more people than he needed. This wasn't true because Jim was soft-hearted or even all that charitably minded—if I had to guess, I'd say Jim Reese was a Republican—no, Jim had grown up thinking like my father does, which is to say that he thought the owner of a business had a responsibility to his workers. Once they were under his care, they became like children—nieces and nephews, at least—and he was required to treat them accordingly. Or at least that was the explanation I came up with for the pair of layabouts that roamed the gravel-covered section of Skinner's Nursery.

The leader was a simpleton named Gus K. "K" because no one could spell or pronounce his last name. Eight or nine or ten letters; I think there was a Z in there, and three vowels might have lined up next to one another. Gus K had an IQ of about 80, which actually might have suited someone in his role, had that person also been blessed with something like work ethic. But Gus K spent most of the days he was supposed to be taking care of plants wandering the premises, his lazy eye seeking out a sympathetic ear for his complaints about how much he was having to work, and how little he was getting paid for it.

Gus K's sidekick was a lanky high school dropout who looked like the lead singer of Incubus and who invariably showed up to work in a T-shirt cut into a tank top—the 19-year-old you hope your daughter won't fall for when she's 16. Add in two ladies in charge of potting, two Mexicans who worked hard but didn't speak a lick of English, a strapping, square-headed man named Dave who taught me how to shovel decorative gravel without snapping a vertebra, and there you had it: the staff at Skinner's Nursery.

And then there was me.

On my first summer weekday on the lot, I wandered through the rows and rows of trees and shrubs, hoping someone would tell me what to do. When no one did, I did what I thought any reasonable employee would do—I asked the boss.

When I knocked, Jim's eyes shot to mine from the work orders and receipts he was studying. I explained why I was standing there: I didn't know what I was supposed to be doing. He considered my plight for a few seconds before standing and grabbing a jacket.

"Come on," he said.

We walked through the inner building to the yard and Jim commandeered a Bobcat (one of those smallish earth-movers you see on landscaping jobs). He explained that we needed to move a bunch of freshly potted trees from one section of the property to another. We got to work and the day passed: him telling me what to do, me sometimes performing that thing correctly.

The next day, I went back to Jim's office. This time, he told me to ask Young Brandon Boyd what needed done.

"That should keep you busy for a while," he said as he walked away.

He was right. Young Brandon Boyd was all too eager to find a willing assistant. He pointed at the rows and rows of round, plastic pots with young trees and shrubs in them.

"You see all those?"

I nodded.

"Well, they need to be watered every day."

The network of hoses at Skinner's made me think of space exploration. Each of us connected to a hose was also connected to the main building. Let go, and you'd be lost. Or maybe this was just one of the many ways I kept myself from losing my mind, as I stood in the sun, holding the long sprayer attachment above each plant for three or four seconds before moving the apparatus a few inches left, right, up, down, to wherever the next plant was. It was mind-numbing, soul-crushing work—mind-numbing, soul-crushing work that I'd soon look back upon fondly.

On my next day at Skinner's, the rain clouds that had hovered over the Kansas River valley since dawn broke loose and took over for our hoses and nozzles. Everyone else went to the break room, a place I didn't like much thanks to the smell of fertilizer and, whenever Gus K and Young Brandon Boyd were eating, the oddly graphic conversations about whatever women they'd somehow lured into their houses the previous weekend. Or said they had.

I went to ask Jim if there was anything I could do.

Once again, he looked up from some paperwork.

Once again, he grabbed a jacket.

Once again, he said, "Come on."

We walked outside and I pulled my own jacket close to guard against the heavy raindrops that, from the looks of it, were going to mean no one was going to have to water any plants for a few days. Jim and I trudged to the very back of the yard, and he showed me inside one of the "lath" houses—half-moon-shaped greenhouses made of clear plastic and two-by-four that also looked like they would have been at home on another planet.

When we were inside, Jim explained that this was where all the plants that would eventually end up in the yard got their start. Then he grabbed one.

"See these weeds?"

I inspected the rumpled surface of dirt where a few tiny green shoots had broken through.

"These little plants can't handle them. They're too small. So I need them pulled." He handed me the pot. "That's where you come in."

I looked at the pot, and then down the length of the lath house, which seemed to stretch to a point at the far end.

"All of them?" I said.

"All of them."

It wasn't so bad, that first day. The rain outside was calming, and I quickly figured out that an upturned five-gallon bucket made a pretty good seat. But by Day Two, the warning signs were red and blinky: this wasn't a job I was born for. At their respective peaks, the lath houses were six feet tall. I was already 6'4". And I was rarely pulling weeds underneath the houses' peaks—that's where the walkway was. I could usually be found under the far edge where the ceiling was only three or four feet off the ground. I looked like a hermit crab, scuttling around, my prey the stubborn weeds in the tiny plastic containers. Weeds that didn't stay gone, mind you. By the time I finished a house, weeds had already started to grow at the start. I was starting to miss my space hose.

Oh, and there were eight of these lath houses. But surely I wouldn't have to weed *all* of them-

"Why yes," Jim said. "This is your new job."

To combat the crushing boredom that hung over my work life like the cloud in a Peanuts comic strip, I used the Sony boombox that sat on my desk at home (compact disc AND dual-cassette, thank you very much) to make tapes of all ten CDs I owned so, for use in the knock-off Discman that I now carried to work like a lunch pail. My other strategy for time-killing was a personal reward system I perfected over the course of several weeks. After my first hour of weeding, I allowed myself to go inside and get a drink of water. After another hour and a half, I could buy an Orange Slice at the pop machine. Then came lunch, with Gus K telling lies about exploits with some woman who had to have been named Kathy or Debbie. In the afternoon, another water break, and then, around 3:30, I visited the gum machine. A quarter got me 17 or 18 chiclets of various flavors. My decisions regarding which to chew next ate up at least fifteen minutes.

With the help of my homemade tapes and the gum and the water-and-Slice breaks, I survived the worst of the summer. Soon enough, the weeds weren't growing so fast, and Young Brandon Boyd put me back on watering which, by contrast, was almost like a vacation.

When the summer ended, I told Jim thanks for the job and said I'd talk to him next spring about the following summer—a variation on "I'll think about it." But this time, I was telling a lie. I hated my job at Skinner's so much that I got teary-eyed some nights at the thought of going to work the next day, probably because I'd finished some of my days with spasms in my wrist thanks to all the weed-pulling.

I didn't talk to Jim Reese until I saw him at church a year and a half later, after I'd put under my belt a summer at Four Seasons Family Pools & Spas. I asked Jim why he'd assigned me such an awful duty as pulling weeds in those lath houses.

"Hell, I don't know," he said with a laugh. "I was paying you minimum wage. But you kept asking me if I needed something done. And since you kept asking, I was glad to oblige."

"But that job you gave me was brutal."

He held up a finger.

"Let that be a lesson to you, son: if you don't want the worst job in the place, don't ask the boss what he needs done. You gotta learn to go with the flow."

His words helped crystallize something that had been floating around in my head while I was pulling weeds. It was clear that I wasn't made for a life pulling weeds, or anything, really, that involved such routine monotony. So I decided I would become a professional basketball player. I didn't tell anyone

about this decision because people from Meriden, Kansas, do not become professional basketball players. People from Meriden, Kansas, don't even like it when people make ludicrous claims about wanting to become professional basketball players. Instead of talking about my plans, I disguised them. In college, I got an engineering degree because that was Responsible. I told people I was thinking of going to graduate school after college. But deep down, I knew: one day, I would play basketball for money. In part because I loved playing basketball, but also because I knew that when I got there, I wouldn't have to worry about asking the boss what to do because what basketball players need to do is
pretty obvious.

So I'd solved that little problem. But that didn't mean I'd fixed everything. I still had a lot to learn when it came to the reason I'd gotten myself into the mess at Skinner's: girls.

The next winter, Kelly Stepka's powers of vexation boomeranged back around to me, and we went to Winter Formal together. She wore a tan dress that showed off her hipbones and I wondered if Kelly and I might become an item—an even more attractive possibility senior year as Kelly had not gotten *worse* looking. This wonderment did not, however, cause me to worry about getting a job or making any plans. Because fuuuuuck that. If Kelly wanted to make me her boyfriend, it would happen not because of the plans I could make or the things I would buy her, but because Kelly liked me how I was.

I congratulated myself on my newfound apathy.

I'd learned something from Jim Reese!

I was going with the flow!

This was going to work!

Then, three days after Winter Formal, Kelly dropped me again and began dating Jed Traxler, a relationship that resulted in the disappearance of Kelly's virginity, a bit of magic I'd always imagined having a role in (although I wasn't sure how).

Kelly and Jed stayed together through prom, and graduation, and they gave it a shot from long distance as freshmen in college: her at Kansas State, him at the University of Kansas.

I was tempted, in my second round of Stepka Heartbreak,

to think Jim Reese had been wrong. After all, I'd gone with the flow, just like he'd said. And it hadn't worked. Not even close.

But that would have been a shortsighted interpretation of the facts because it's not just going with the flow that counts. You also need to have the sort of flow that someone wants to go with. Teenaged Kelly Stepka was never going to be the right girl for teenaged me. I needed the kind of girl who would think it cute that I wrote out a cue card for a conversation. The kind of girl who would have questions of her own, on our way to the movies. The kind of girl who would have an answer, if I asked her who she thought was going to come to her funeral. (Specifically: that she wondered if maybe, just maybe, I'd be there.)

Or the kind of girl who will be mildly impressed that I don't break character when MC Hammer thinks I'm Matt Leinart. The kind of girl who will laugh at my story about Jim Reese and Kelly Stepka. The kind of girl who, when the party is over, will come back to my room at the Bellagio, where we-

-do a bunch of dry-humping until four in the morning.

Not exactly an outcome befitting a newly drafted NFL quarterback.

But just about the right outcome for someone who's spent part of the night pretending to be one.

CAMERON

A Thursday afternoon

I need to time this exactly right. And timing this exactly right is going to involve:

A) Pretending I didn't see her as soon as she pulled up to the gas pump outside.

B) Pretending I haven't been hoping she'd come inside since I saw her get out of her tan Toyota 4Runner.

C) Pretending I haven't been rehearsing what I'll say in this moment, as she walks by with a tray of French fries, looking for somewhere to sit.

I wait until she's almost past me, her eyes on a seat inside the deserted Wendy's you see attached to gas stations all over Midwestern interstates.

I beg her pardon. Her blond hair whirls and her gray eyes meet mine.

I wave at the white plastic chair across from me.

"I know this is a little weird, but, uh, do you want to have the most white-trash date of all time?"

I'm holding my breath, because maybe she'll find it funny and maybe she'll find it scary. She checks the rest of the Wendy's, possibly to see if there's anyone better, possibly to see if anyone is watching this exchange. Then she shrugs and says OK, and we do indeed have the most white-trash date of all time: two strangers, tired of their respective drives, dumping triglycerides into their bodies.

She tells me she's headed back to school after a weekend in Kansas City. She's a graduate student at Northern Iowa.

"So you're used to that?" I ask, pointing outside, where the wind is whipping snow across the steppes of north Missouri. Not new, flaky snow, mind you. Old, gritty snow that's been on the ground for days.

"You can never get used to that."

She asks me what I'm doing on I-35 and I tell her: I'm driving to Iowa to let my college orthopedist have a look at my left knee, which started clicking, popping, and catching during summer league with the Minnesota Timberwolves.

The television pilot is dead after we spent 3.6 million of Fox's dollars to make something that resembled a *Scrubs* knockoff, but on a basketball court. I've left Los Angeles because I have no reason to be there.

And so basketball is back because I'll take loneliness and an uncertain future over television executives and their race to the bottom.

She shakes her head.

"You're driving all the way to Iowa to see a doctor?"

"It's hard to find ones you can trust," I tell her.

When our burgers are done (we each say we would never eat at Wendy's under normal circumstances, but perhaps we are each lying), I ask for her number.

"Maybe you'll be back in Kansas City someday," I say.

I can tell that she's mildly impressed, not by me, per se, but by my boldness, as Midwestern girls sometimes are.

She gives me her number, and then we have a half-hug and get into our cars. As we pull out of the parking lot, I realize that this isn't my first time talking to a grad student at this gas station. The bus stopped here on the trip I took north with Shelly McQuaid.

After ten minutes of following the 4Runner up I-35, I call the grad student from Northern Iowa.

"I was hoping I'd hear from you," she says after three rings.

I smile into the phone, but then there is silence.

"Uh," I say.

She laughs.

"Right? We talked about the small stuff."

"And we've got a long drive ahead."

"One time," she says. "Someone sat down next to me at a party and said, 'Big talk or no talk.' I knew she would be my friend. So, big talk or no talk?"

I glance out at the Iowa night that is rapidly approaching.

"Big talk it is. What do you want to hear about?"

"Well, you said you played basketball in this town we're coming up on. Tell me a story about that."

I consider telling her about Shelly and the bus ride. But I quickly come to my senses; she doesn't want to hear that she's not the first girl I've picked up on I-35.

And anyway, there's another story I'd like to tell her—a complicated one I haven't told anyone in a long time because it's a hard one to tell. But there's something about strangers that opens us up; sometimes it's easier to tell the truth to a neighbor on your airplane than a neighbor on your street.

"How about a mystery?"

"I like the sound of that."

"OK," I say. "So here's the setting for this mystery: I was a junior in college, sitting in my usual study spot at the tables on the third floor at the library."

"What were you studying?"

"Something terrible—fluids or thermodynamics."

"Sounds thrilling."

"Riveting. So anyway, I'm sitting there studying and this girl walks over. Now, at the time probably 80% of the student population at Iowa State knows my name. But that didn't mean I wasn't excited about girls walking over to my study table."

"You're a dude. You've got a dick."

"I'm a dude. I've got a dick."

"So what does she say, this girl?"

"She says, 'You're Paul Shirley, right?'"

"Good opener for you."

"Yeah, not terrible. So I nod at her, hoping I'll look like I'm being cool, but really I didn't know what to say."

"Oh, you boys."

"We're the worst. Especially when we're 21."

"I'll never date anyone under 30 again."

"That's astute of you. So this girl, she's got a picture of me, and she holds it out and says, 'Would you sign this for me?'"

"Sounds pretty cool."

"Yeah, except that I did not want to sign this picture of me. At all. In fact, I never wanted to see it again."

"Why not?"

"Well, that's the mystery."

7

Double Heartbreak

On February 24, 2000, after a fast break during a home basketball game against the University of Texas, I came down awkwardly on my right foot. Twenty minutes later, I was on an X-ray table inside the clinic where my blood pressure had once been measured at diabetic levels before my second-ever sex act.

My shoulders were slumped and my eyes were on my hands in my lap because a technician had just told me that he could see a crack in the fifth metatarsal in my right foot.

I'd spent most of my life hoping I would someday play for a great college basketball team. For a while, my wish had come true. At the time of my injury, we were ranked 19th in the country, had lost only four times all season, and were on our way to the school's first regular season conference championship.

Now, just as my team was about to earn its highest-ever seed in the NCAA Tournament, I was relegated to the sidelines in one of those hard plastic walking boots that look like the snow boots the cooler kids had when I was eight.

My broken foot wasn't a career-killing injury, though, and there was reason to be hopeful that, with some rehabilitative work, I would be able to return in time for some portion of the NCAA Tournament. I reported daily to the training facility just north of Iowa State's football field, where I was reacquainted with the SwimEx: a nine-foot by fifteen-foot pool that acts as an aquatic treadmill. Thanks to my ischial stress fracture the previous year and a tibial stress fracture at the beginning of this one, my junior season, I knew the SwimEx like a psych patient knows a straightjacket.

There was acupuncture, too, and a machine purported to encourage bone growth, and a lot of wringing of hands and gnashing of teeth. Mostly by me, but some by everyone involved; I wasn't as integral to our success as my teammate and future NBA draft pick Marcus Fizer, but I had been worth eight points and six rebounds every game that season.

While my teammates kept winning—a first-round NCAA Tournament game against Central Connecticut State, a second-round game against Auburn—I stayed in the SwimEx, lofty goals seeping into my brain. Somehow, I would surprise everyone, come back earlier than expected, and have some spectacular impact on our tournament chances.

Every few days during my rehab, I saw the team orthopedist, who would, six, seven, and eight years after my college career, perform my first, second, and fourth orthopedic surgeries. Three weeks after the injury, he told me he wasn't sure it was a *good* idea for me to play, but that he also wasn't sure it would do any more damage if I did.

In other words, it was up to me.

I knew that playing on broken bones probably wasn't a prescription for my long-term health. But then my teammates dismantled UCLA in the Sweet Sixteen, setting up a game between us and big, bad, number-one seeded Michigan State, home to future pros Mateen Cleaves, Morris Peterson, Charlie Bell, and Jason Richardson.

No analyst worth his salt gave us a chance.

I had to play in this basketball game.

When I tell stories of my basketball past, people will sometimes ask, "So what did your parents think of the game?"

This question is based on the assumption that my parents attended every important basketball game I ever played, which would have been a reasonable assumption only if my parents had no other children and did not have jobs.

My mother and father had driven to Minneapolis for Iowa State's first- and second-round games (those games in which I didn't play) and had plans to attend if we made it to the Mecca of college basketball achievement: the Final Four. But obligations on the home front kept them from our Regional Final game against Michigan State: my brother Matt had just led his high school basketball team to the state tournament and was trying to decide on a college, and my brother Tom was in third grade, doing whatever it is that third-graders do. Long division, probably.

That isn't to say that I wasn't without familial support in Michigan. My uncle Tom (my mother's brother) and his son, my cousin, came all the way from Los Angeles to the Palace at Auburn Hills for our Elite Eight game against Michigan State.

I admired my uncle more than almost anyone in the world; he'd lived the sort of life to which I aspired. He'd been a hippie in college—a scholarship kid at Harvard. He'd ridden a motorcycle across the country, much to the chagrin of his mother, my grandmother. He'd traveled widely, read voraciously, and when he'd shown me the helipad at the top of the hospital in Los Angeles where he was a cardiac surgeon, I'd decided then and there that I would be a cardiac surgeon, too. (I was 12 and not yet aware of my own squeamishness around blood.)

My uncle Tom was more like what I wanted to be than my own father, who seemed comparatively boring in the way that those in our immediate family can seem to us, as if they are a picture held so close that we can only see the pixels that make it up.

But that wasn't the entirety of the emotional knot that tied me to my uncle. He also served as an unwitting emissary from the grave.

My mother's childhood had been cursed by tragedy. Her father died when she was 12, which was hard enough, but also not nearly as horrifying as what was to come: the death, at age 17, of the middle child, Jim.

According to the stories I heard when I was a kid, Jim had been The One: a naturally talented football player and track star who balanced his sporting prowess with easy wit and a bright smile, characteristics displayed in my grandmother's favorite story about her lost son.

Before a game of strip poker at the neighbors' house, Jim donned several layers of women's undergarments, setting up a punch line that arrived in a different way than he'd planned. On the walk to the neighbors' house, Jim's appendix burst. When the paramedics got to the scene and started cutting through his clothes, Jim kept quiet, playing the part of the obedient patient, until they discovered the bras and panties underneath, and he could take it no more.

"What do you think?" he'd asked through a burst of laughter. "These look good on me?"

Jim died in a car crash in Colorado after his first semester of college. I'd always felt the weight his death had dropped onto my mother's family, in the form of the way they were with each other, and me. They weren't a demonstratively loving group anyway, all products of Swedish and German stoicism. But after the dual tragedies of a lost father and husband, brother and son, they'd turned inward even more sharply. It was a rare trick, indeed, to get my mother or her brother to crack into a show of spontaneous emotion.

It was with all of this lurking somewhere in the deep recesses of my mind that, on the way to the scorer's table to check into the game against Michigan State, I spied Uncle Tom and his son, Jim's namesake, in the crowd, twenty rows back, straight up from our bench.

Tom smiled, an Iowa State cap over the hairline that had receded sometime during his cardiology residency.

He mouthed "Good seats!" with a raised right thumb.

Then he pointed at his butt and raised his eyebrows. He was asking how the Toradol was working.

I gave him a thumbs-up of my own; the shot I'd gotten in the locker room had hurt, but my foot no longer did. In fact, I couldn't feel my right leg.

After that moment, the game against Michigan State exists in my brain only in flashes of clarity. It seems, by my memory's telling, that I played almost the entire game. But in truth, I played only 16 minutes. It also seems like I contributed more, statistically, than I did. But I had only four points, four rebounds and two assists.

Some of this dissonance can be attributed to personal bias: my impact on the game seems more important to me because it was me, duh. But I can also be forgiven some of my revisionist history because I was involved in one of the most memorable plays in Iowa State basketball history.

With two minutes left, I looked up at the scoreboard as I jogged across the half-court line, doing the calculations.

We were ahead by one.

We were playing well.

There wasn't much time left.

Conclusion: *We might go the Final Four!*

All game, our All-American point guard, Brooklyn playground legend Jamaal Tinsley, had confounded the Michigan State guards with his ballhandling wizardry, and Marcus Fizer had bullied his way to the basket, like he always did. We'd neutralized Michigan State's powerful offense and had kept the heavily partisan crowd out of the game. (We were playing only an hour from Michigan State's campus; of the 22,000 fans in attendance, 20,000 were wearing Michigan State green.)

And now, on the right side of the court, Tinsley had spotted me cutting through the lane to the basket—a crafty little maneuver that was facilitated by my defender's focus on my more-talented teammates. Jamaal whipped me the ball. Then, sensing that a defender would soon arrive to interfere with my progress, I flipped that ball toward the rim just before that defender materialized under me.

We crashed to the floor together, but I looked up to find the ball dipping cleanly through the net. I glanced to my right, where a referee was signaling what could only be the right call: a blocking foul on the Michigan State player who hadn't given me time to come down from my Toradol-aided leap. On the floor, I did the math. My two points, plus our one-point lead, meant we were now up three. If I made the free throw, we'd go ahead by four.

That trip to the Final Four—a trip I'd dreamed of since whooping and hollering after watching Danny Manning and Kansas beat the University of Oklahoma in the 1988 edition—was looking all the more likely. And what sweet vindication that trip would be after a year spent in psychological misery, enduring daily doses of a couple of superstar teammates I couldn't stand, a coach who screamed at us like we were prisoners of war, and recovery from two separate broken bones—one of which had required the recent hasty rehabilitation that had gotten me here.

But no matter: I'd done it!

And in front of my uncle, who had to be on the edge of his seat, his placid demeanor finally rifted by the excitement I'd just generated inside the Palace.

Then I looked to my left, where I saw a different referee doing something odd. He was signaling that he'd seen an offensive foul, and was—rather demonstrably—waving off the basket. But that didn't make sense; the Michigan State player hadn't given me any room to land. Everyone knows I had to have space to land!

With the crowd screeching in a manner that would become familiar to me during the European segments of coming basketball adventures, the referees huddled up, and kept huddling, and kept huddling. I feigned nonchalance, milling toward the bench for water as I watched the referees discuss my fate. If the call went against me, my basket would be waved off, Michigan State would get the ball AND the momentum, and my small-town dreams of playing in a Final Four might be dashed forever. There was also this little detail: I'd had four fouls before the collision. If the referees called the foul on me, I was finished for the game. And, while I am prone to self-deprecation and while it might seem that I was an unreliable cog in the Iowa State machine, what with that broken foot and a lower body full of Toradol, I was always the sort of player a coach wants on the court at the end of the game, even a sadist like Larry Eustachy.

But I wasn't going to have to worry about any of that, was I? Surely, they'd put it together: when I'd gone up for the shot, the guy hadn't been there. When I'd come down, he had. It was a foul on him, and they were just making sure. Weren't they?

I looked over at Eustachy, who was chewing his lip and asking his assistants what was taking so long. I tried to find my uncle but quickly realized it was impossible; everyone in the place was standing and screaming, their loyalties on full display. Then, after what didn't just seem like an eternity but was, by basketball standards, the head referee jogged over to the scorer's table to make the call.

Most colleges' fan bases believe themselves to be the "best." This is a ludicrous claim, a little like thinking the T-shirt your kids got you—the one proclaiming you the "World's #1 Dad!"—is accurate.

Iowa State fans are no different. They think, because they are devoted and dedicated, that they are The Best. They are not. Most university teams' fans are devoted and dedicated. However, Iowa State fans *are* among the most loyal and protective I've seen in a long career around basketball people. They also have great memories. If I meet an Iowa State fan out in the wild, there is a better-than-average chance that he or she will ask me about the call that head referee made on that day in March.

The call in question was this one: a double foul.

A foul on me, and a foul on my Michigan State defender. This call was problematic for many reasons, not the least of which being that There Is No Such Thing As A Double Foul.

But more germane to the gameflow: the foul gave me the aforementioned disqualification, it negated the basket, and it took the ball away from us.

I wandered in disbelief to our bench, watching our assistant coaches restrain Coach Eustachy, who looked like a Doberman on methamphetamines. He wasn't alone. If the game had been happening in Des Moines, someone would have murdered one of the referees on the spot, not just because the call hadn't been kind to us, but also because it was a call without precedent, without logic, really. Even if the foul *was* on me (which it wasn't, dammit), it couldn't *also* be on him.

The thing of it was, though, that while we had lost a couple of points that—according to me and every Iowa State fan in the world—should have been ours, we still had the lead. And we still had Jamaal Tinsley and Marcus Fizer and a bunch of other very good basketball players.

Or so I told myself, as I took a seat at the end of the bench, my game over, the Toradol wearing off instantly. Emotional deflation has a weird way of rendering useless most opiates.

My optimism was short-lived. On the next play, Michigan State rushed downcourt and ran a play for a successful Morris Peterson dunk. The crowd erupted, volcanic after an entire game of forced dormancy. A few more plays engineered by the Flintstones—as CBS commentator Verne Lundquist was apt to calling the Flint-spawned trio of Peterson, Charlie Bell, and the lantern-jawed Mateen Cleaves—and my hopes of a Final Four appearance evaporated like the Toradol in my body.

In most basketball games, there is a period of time between the moment the outcome is determined and the game's actual end. The clock still has to wind down to make the game official. In *this* game, that period of time should have lasted about thirty seconds. But it did not.

With a few seconds left, Eustachy stormed onto the court. He was infuriated in part by The Double Foul, in part by other calls that hadn't gone our way, and in part by the general feeling he and we got, which was that no one wanted him and lowly Iowa State in the Final Four, at least not when the camera-ready Tom Izzo and Michigan State were available.

Eustachy let loose with an expletive-rich tirade and was thrown out of the game, which would cost him a one-game suspension the next season.

It was, by far, the most I'd ever liked him.

Meanwhile, at the end of the bench, there was me. I'd been able to hold out hope even as our miniscule lead had shrunk from one to minus-five. But as the last seconds rolled off the clock and it became clear that there would be no miraculous comeback, the dam behind my eyes burst.

I tried to cover up, first with my jersey, then with my hand, telling myself that this wasn't the place for a scene. But emotions rarely listen to logic. I couldn't stop thinking about how close we'd gotten—about how close *I'd* gotten—to making a childhood dream come true, to being a hero, to doing all of it in front of my uncle.

When the buzzer sounded, I staggered into the locker room, where Eustachy said something that was supposed to help. There were reporters, and many of them probably thought it was ridiculous that I was still crying so hard. If I'd been one of them, I would have thought the same. It *was* only a game, after all.

Later, after ten minutes or twenty minutes or two hours, an assistant coach put a hand on my shoulder and told me I needed to get my shoes off, at least. The touch brought me out of my sad reverie; I might have been shattered inside, but I was also becoming a spectacle—the only one left in the locker room.

I unlaced my left shoe, and then my right, and put my feet on the floor, marveling at how much the broken bone in the right one hurt.

I hobbled to the bay of showers and allowed the water to carry some of the pain down the drain. Afterward, I put on the Iowa State tracksuit I'd worn to the arena like the rest of my teammates, back when we'd been worthy of a police escort through the darkening streets of Auburn Hills. I picked up my bag, gave myself permission for one of those snorts that come after you've spilled all the tears you can, and walked into the cavernous hallway outside our locker room. An NCAA official pointed me toward the bus, and I started down the long concrete tunnel, an image of that Mean Joe Greene commercial from my childhood flashing across my brain. I allowed myself to feel like I was some kind of gladiator, and by the time I got to the ramp where our bus was waiting to take us away from the Palace, I was breathing normally again.

I was only a junior.

I had another year.

We would be back.

I weaved through a crush of Iowa State fans, all of them trying to clap me on the back on my way to the bus. I nodded at their applause, trying to say thanks without saying anything, telling myself to keep moving, that I was almost there, that I could rest again when I got inside.

Then I felt myself gripped by a bear hug.

"I'm so proud of you," my uncle managed to say, before he choked up and put his hand to his face.

I wasn't done crying just yet.

We probably flew back to Ames but for all I know, we took a submarine. We got home on a Saturday night, and I felt bad enough to allow myself to be dragged out on the town. I didn't drink anything, of course, because I never did back then. I did run into Shelly McQuaid, the girl who'd been responsible for my elevated blood pressure that day we were going to have sex a second time, at a bar in Campustown. She was in town visiting her parents. We made a plan to meet for breakfast the next day.

At breakfast, my first love, who'd kept her left hand under the table for most of our meal, finally showed me the ring there. I wasn't devastated, or even surprised, but it wasn't exactly what

I needed to see two days after my world had come apart like the bridge Gandalf shatters to save the hobbits. I told her I was happy for her, and we ate, and then I got the hell out of there, anxious to find refuge in my apartment.

Once I was home and mummified by blankets on the couch, I called my mother for a debriefing. After we digested everything that had happened as best we could, she changed the subject, slightly, to tell me she was hearing from relatives all over the country. They'd seen my picture in the papers.

When I'd started crying in Auburn Hills, there had been plenty of cameras around to capture my pain. There was one photo of me, in particular—a photo of my desperate, distraught, tear-mangled face, held up sort of half-assedly by one hand that was running through my hair.

They'd used the picture as far away as Dallas and Los Angeles, my mother told me.

"Well," I said with a sigh. "You should probably get a copy, to show my wife someday."

When we hung up, I went back to the blankets to continue my psychological rehabilitation.

By Monday morning, that rehabilitation seemed almost complete and I woke up feeling almost optimistic. I *was* only a junior. I *had* done everything I could. And I didn't have to go to practice, which meant my broken foot would only hurt "a lot" as opposed to "all of the amounts."

I got out of bed, brushed my teeth, washed my face, and gathered my books. We may have been busy inspiring most of a sports-mad state with a run nearly to the Final Four, but that didn't mean my engineering classes were canceled. I left my apartment at 7:15 for the walk to Friley Hall, where I planned to start my day off with a heavy-duty breakfast meant to keep on the 20 pounds I'd gained in the past two years.

I slipped through Friley's front door and reached into the wooden newsstand where, every day that year, I'd picked up a copy of the *Iowa State Daily* to read with breakfast. Today's stack was no different from those other stacks—it was about three-quarters of the way up the smooth wooden bay, polished by year-after-year of newspaper in, newspaper out.

The paper itself, though—that was a little different.

My picture was on the front page.

But it wasn't just *on* the front page. It *was* the front page—a front page that was going to be seen by approximately 24,000 of my fellow students this day.

I froze while I considered my options. The first to come to mind involved turning for home and crawling back into bed. My GPA was good enough, wasn't it? I could afford a missed class or two.

But I pushed aside that thought with another. *Don't take yourself so seriously.*

As I walked toward the trays, I laughed for the sake of the people who had the nerve to point at me and then at their copies of the newspaper. I ate my breakfast, I put my tray away, I went to class.

And then, midway through the morning, I went to the library to study, where the curious girl came over with her copy of the *Daily* in hand.

She asked me if I was me, and I was left to wonder what to do.

I thought, briefly, about asking her to rethink her manners, because even if she didn't recognize that it had obviously been a weekend that landed on the spectrum of Terrible somewhere between Fairly and Extremely, she probably should have recognized that I couldn't have been thrilled to have my tear-stained visage on the front of the campus newspaper and, further, that asking me to sign a copy of that newspaper might not be the best way to help me through what was probably going to be a rather difficult day.

But the girl in front of me didn't want me to explain all that. She didn't want to know about the stories and emotions and complex feelings that went into those tears that were rolling down my cheeks in the photo she was holding. To her, it was simpler than that. I existed on the other end of the camera's lens, compartmentalized and categorized like a plane crash or a runway model. It was important to her that I maintained the illusion—that I pretended my tears were entirely about her and her fandom, and not something more nuanced, like personal battles and familial history. That was the trade-off sports trafficked in. I cared about the game I played for a set of wide-ranging reasons, which drove some kind of fire in me. She, in turn, pretended I was playing for her. That's why she hadn't thought about my feelings when she asked if I would sign a photo of me at my very worst.

This wasn't about me. This was about her.

However, I wasn't going to be able to explain any of that just then. Maybe I'd have a chance, someday, like when I had a few hours to kill on a drive up I-35, talking to a graduate student I met in a rest-stop Wendy's, whom I would see only one more time when she was in Kansas City to visit her friends.

But not in the Parks library on the campus of Iowa State University, on a Monday morning that I wanted desperately to turn normal.

So what I did was this:

I smiled.

I said, "Sure."

I signed her newspaper.

I told her to have a nice day.

And then I went back to Thermodynamics. And she went back to believing that I'd been crying because we lost to Michigan State in the NCAA Tournament.

MINNEAPOLIS

A Sunday evening

The cartilage behind my patella was wearing away.

I drove back to Iowa for my first knee surgery.

I did two months of physical therapy.

I reported to training camp with the Minnesota Timberwolves.

Now, after four weeks in training camp, I know a lot more about my status with the Timberwolves.

Yesterday, at the end of a plane ride home from a preseason game with the Milwaukee Bucks, the team's general manager sat down next to me and soon after, the Timberwolves became the sixth NBA team to release, cut, or otherwise send me packing, joining the Los Angeles Lakers, the New Orleans Hornets, the Chicago Bulls, the Phoenix Suns, and the Atlanta Hawks (twice).

And so, it is time to go. Again.

I'm explaining all of this to a girl from Minneapolis I met at a sports bar after my first week of camp.

Back then, there'd been hope.

Now there is none, and I can see that she's recoiling, detaching from the loser in the car next to her.

And this means my plan is going badly.

My plan, you see, is to get her back to the hotel room where I've lived for the past month. It's a nice hotel room. It looks out on one of the main streets of Minneapolis. It has already been covered in snow twice since I've been here.

You might think I want to get her back to my hotel room to have sex with her. This is not entirely untrue. But mostly, I want her to come back to the hotel room, get under some blankets with me, and tell me everything will be OK.

This is my secret: I just want someone to tell me it will be OK.

I can't tell her this, of course. I don't have any right to expect reassurance out of her, so I'm not surprised when she says that it's been nice to meet me, that we should stay in touch, that she wishes me good luck.

We kiss, briefly, and she gets out of the car.

I start back to the hotel.

I make one stop on the way.

When I get inside my hotel room, I drop the brown paper bag on the bed.

I take out its contents, put on my headphones, and click over to an album by Cat Power.

And this time, I tell myself the story.

8

What Goes Around Comes Around
(But Sometimes Takes a While)

In 1984, *Cheers* kicked off its third season, the last with Coach Ernie Pantusso. That summer, Bruce Springsteen's *Born in the U.S.A.* hit number one, staying there for surprisingly short stint of only four weeks before being supplanted by *Purple Rain*. Neither of these events had much bearing on my life because in 1984 I was six years old, and it would be fifteen years before I understood that "Born in the U.S.A." was actually a protest song, twenty-five before I saw an episode of *Cheers* from beginning to end.

In fact, there were very few things that happened in 1984 that had real impact on my life. One of the exceptions was the founding of *Beckett Baseball Card Monthly*. The timing was no coincidence. All over the United States, little boys like me were going mad for packs of cardboard squares featuring pictures of our favorite ballplayers on front, their statistics on the back.

I suspect this baseball card boom had a little to do with nascent globalization—it was easier than ever to get cards into stores—and a little to do with baseball's popularity in the late '70s and '80s. Television had brought baseball into living rooms in ubiquitous fashion. And, because it was before the era of 57 channels and nothing on, there weren't many options besides watching one's local ball-playing heroes on the tube.

But the boom also had a lot to do with the people buying cards for their kids. My father, like many fathers of the age, had a story typical of his generation: "If my stepmom hadn't thrown out all those cards of mine, they'd have probably been worth a mint!"

This was a man who'd worked nights for the Rock Island Railroad to pay for junior college, who'd used the GI Bill to pay for graduate school.

My dad was not one for hyperbole.

My father's initial contributions to my baseball card habit were small: a pack of Topps for my brothers and me on the occasional payday. But it didn't take much to create an addiction. In a pre-Internet age, those tiny slabs of cardboard were like passports to another world.

To say I plowed my allowance into baseball cards would be inaccurate, largely because I didn't get an allowance and so didn't have much money to plow into anything. But what little money I did have—well, baseball cards were certainly at the top of the To-Buy List.

I bought individual packs—Topps, Fleer, Donruss, Upper Deck (in the nineties). I asked for full sets for Christmas; two years later, the 1987 Donruss set I got was worth five times the $25 my parents paid for it. I went to baseball card shows with Darin Densmore and his father, where we would lust after Rated Rookies and "error" cards, like the one where someone at Fleer hadn't noticed that Billy Ripken had "Fuck Face" written on the knob of his bat.

By seventh grade, I had built up a formidable collection. I didn't focus on the popular or valuable cards; I was intent on collecting the cards of players I liked. This was of particular importance in my family because an unspoken rule amongst my brothers and me stated that once someone had decided he was collecting a player's cards, that player was off-limits to the other brothers. This didn't mean I had to surrender all of my Ryne Sandbergs to my brother Dan; it just meant that, if I had a Ryne Sandberg card, I was expected by these unwritten rules to trade it to Dan at fair market value. (And under no circumstance was I to start a competing collection of Ryne Sandbergs.)

My brothers and I kept our cards in pristine shape, organizing them in binders specially made for the job. Each plastic sheet inside was three cards across by three cards down. We organized and re-organized our cards religiously, first by player, then by year, then by value. Sometimes we got our hands on a copy of a "Beckett," as *Beckett Baseball Card Monthly* was called for short, and put the cards' values on Post-its that we stuck to the fronts of their holders.

My baseball card collection provided me with hours of entertainment that, in retrospect, seems far more related to accounting than to fun; I was worried about cards' value, and players' batting averages, and whether they'd been born in 1965 or 1968.

My collection also provided me with something I never expected: a shot at revenge.

The Jefferson West school district that oversaw my education in algebra, cursive, and rejection at the hands of myriad girls in myriad ways is a consolidated school district encompassing the western part of Jefferson County, Kansas. There are two significant (for Jefferson County) towns in the district: Meriden (pop. 700) and Ozawkie (pop. 500). Because of negotiations that, I assume, accompanied the formation of the school district long before I roamed its halls, the elementary and high schools were built in Meriden, while the middle school landed in Ozawkie.

This caused some logistical headaches during my childhood. When I was in middle school, my days started with a 30-minute bus ride from my house to the elementary school in Meriden. There, I transferred to one of three buses that would take us middle schoolers from Meriden to Ozawkie. This extensive commute propped up my reading habit for years. It also introduced me to Eazy-E, who was played on a boombox in the back of the bus by one of my classmates who, curiously, would later turn out to be a fan of country music.

This interim bus ride also provided fertile ground for baseball card trades.

I was afraid of many things in middle school. Girls, school dances, body hair—these developments terrified me, mostly because I wasn't participating in any of them. As such, between the ages of 12 and 17, I was mostly lost. If the mainstream was downtown, I was lurking somewhere in the suburbs, not sure I wanted to get any closer. But there were a few things I still understood. More or less, anything that was a vestige of a more innocent time—a time that wasn't really in the past for me, as my hairless body would attest.

So, while I never contributed a single tape to my Eazy-E-loving classmate's efforts as a boombox DJ, I did huddle around the baseball card books the day after Darin Densmore or Max Phalen announced that "tomorrow's a card day!" It didn't hurt that, relative to most of my fellow collectors, I was a math whiz and so could calculate the fairness (or lack thereof) of a particular trade in seconds. Usually the trades were affairs that would, if we were gangsters in the Forties, be called small potatoes. A four-dollar Juan Gonzalez rookie card for a two-dollar John Olerud and a Bobby Bonilla that was only worth a dollar. Or an '88 Wade Boggs that was worth $2.50 in exchange for a '90 Tom Glavine worth the same.

But sometimes, they got bigger.

The proposal started like all trades anywhere do: one of us expressed interest in something the other had.

In this case, Clint Byrd had a Roger Clemens rookie card in mint condition.

And I wanted it.

I mean, Clemens was destined for the Hall of Fame (or so I—and everyone else—assumed at the time). Plus, Clemens was one of my favorites, and not just because I collected his cards. He was the Mike Tyson of pitchers. He didn't mess around with corners or curve balls or any such nonsense. He just threw it hard. And usually, he threw it right past people. (Clemens did, of course, have a curve ball and assorted other off-speed stuff, but at the time, nuance wasn't my strong suit. Also, I was a skinny kid who was afraid of everything; being blessed with anything people called "overpowering" seemed like the ultimate honor.)

But there was another reason I wanted that card: something Clint Byrd had done to me in third grade.

The grade school principal in charge when I arrived at Jefferson West Elementary for kindergarten was cut of the tyrant cloth of the fifties and sixties. (Something wool-based, I would imagine.) He was himself in his sixties, with close-cropped gray hair and glasses. Everyone in school feared him, which—if the paddle on his wall was any indication—was exactly what he was going for.

It was with great relief, then, that we welcomed a new principal during my second-grade year. Mr. Scotland brought with him a more modern, less combative approach. He learned the kids' names. He talked with us during the day. (He once taught Oliver Bledsoe and me a trick for doing long division while we stood in the lunch line.)

And he took down the paddle.

Mr. Scotland's greatest contribution to Jefferson West Elementary was the Country Store. Born of the movement toward positive reinforcement shepherded into school curricula in the late Seventies, the Country Store was stocked with toys and trinkets that could be purchased using "tokens"—tiny white, plastic discs stamped with our school mascot, a tiger, that were given by teachers to kids who'd behaved or achieved. A teacher might give one of her students a token for holding the door for another kid, or two tokens for doing well on a worksheet, and so on. If it were implemented today, and in most areas of the United States, the Country Store would probably break a school's budget; it would have to be stocked with Xboxes and iPads.

But in rural Kansas in the Eighties, where on the socioeconomic spectrum everyone fell between lower-lower middle class and upper-lower middle class, it didn't take much to get us excited. Ten tokens got you a pencil topper. Twenty, one of those water guns that would probably break after two uses. Thirty minutes on the school's only computer—an early Macintosh—would set you back fifty tokens. At the outer reaches were the high-ticket items: a Walkman, a fancy pen, and the object of my affection—a Sony Dream Machine clock radio.

Cost: 220 tokens.

The introduction of tokens was quite the boon to the overachieving teacher's pet set, a group of which I was the charter member. I was also—no surprise here—a Saver. During childhood, my favorite (and perhaps only) piece of mail was the monthly statement from Credit Union One of Kansas, which would tell me how much interest I'd earned on my savings account. (In my defense, this was the Eighties, when savings accounts brought in six or seven percent. It was like someone was just *giving* me three dollars a month.)

It was an accepted truth that to save anywhere near 220 tokens a kid would have to gather tokens at a steady clip AND save them all year—resisting the temptation to squander ten tokens on, say, an itty-bitty troll doll for the top of his pencil. In third grade I went to work, ignoring instincts that had protected me from ridicule before and answering as many questions as I could. When Mrs. Maloney introduced a dictionary-based game wherein she would call out a word and the first student to find it would get a token, she soon had to institute a rule that prevented anyone from winning more than five tokens.

I kept my booty in a small flannel sack with a drawstring top. This was third grade, so my little baglet lived in my desk: four cast-iron legs and a platform of polished wood that was supported by a piece of iron shaped like a heel cup. Access came in the back, closest to the chair that accompanied the desk.

It wasn't exactly a Brinks truck, and I'm not sure why I was so surprised on the day I found my little bag was gone. I first assumed that my tokens' absence was my fault; maybe I'd taken them somewhere, I thought. But why would I have taken my tokens anywhere? They were scrip in a company town, valueless outside of Jeff West Elementary.

With my head hung like an Old West deputy who'd awakened to find the cattle rustler gone, I walked to Mrs. Maloney's desk and explained that I couldn't find my tokens and was afraid someone might have stolen them.

Mrs. Maloney told me not to worry and called for a confession from my classmates, offering a third-grade teacher's version of diplomatic immunity to anyone who turned in my tokens. But no admission of guilt was made, no sack of tokens was forthcoming, and my heart stayed broken. At last count, I'd had well north of 200 tokens, within easy striking distance of the total I needed. But now it was April. The school year was almost over. There was no way I was going to get that clock radio; at best, I'd maybe be able to hit 40 tokens by summer break.

What haunted me, though, was not knowing what had happened.

Had I done something stupid and left them somewhere?

Had I accidentally dumped them when I was cleaning out old erasers and older globs of glue?

Or had someone gone into my desk and stolen them?

The latter, I learned four years later, when at a middle

school football game Clint Byrd said, "Hey Paul, remember when you thought you'd lost all your tokens back in, like, second gra-"

"Third," I said. "What about it?"

I could feel my heart rate ticking up.

"I took them," Clint said.

During Clint's good-natured confession, he admitted that he'd waited all year for me to build my stash, a farmer greedily eying his biggest pig.

I faked laughs with him, trying to affect the attitude of someone who thought it would be downright silly to remain angry about something so petty, so childish, so small.

On the inside, however:

This motherfucker stole my tokens.

What I'm saying is: yeah, I wanted to fleece Clint Byrd on the baseball card trading block. If I could have gotten away with it, I would have traded him a Buddy Biancalana for a Mickey Mantle rookie card. (Sorry, Buddy Biancalana.)

I happened to have a couple of Ken Griffey, Jr., cards I'd been hoarding for just such an opportunity as this one with Clint Byrd. I didn't have any real affection for Griffey. He was, though, one of the hottest players in baseball. And in baseball cards. Roger Clemens, on the other hand, was, like, old news. This was 1992; he'd already been around for six or seven years. Griffey was new, fresh, exciting, like an unopened box of cereal that you've never had but your mother broke down and bought for you. I proposed that I would give Clint Byrd two Griffey cards plus an older Nolan Ryan (which looked like it should have been worth a lot, but which was worth only a dollar or two) in exchange for the Clemens card. The Griffeys were each worth five or six dollars. With the Ryan card, Clint's haul would be around $13 in value. The Clemens card, though, was worth $26.

"No way, man," Clint said. "That's not even close."

Channeling my inner televangelist, I went to work on his defenses. I pointed out that each of the three cards I was proposing to give him had the potential of increased value, especially because two of them were Griffeys, and who knew what might become of him? (The assumption at the time was Willie Mays, more or less.)

And, yeah, the Clemens card was worth a little more, but it didn't have the long-term potential the Griffeys had.

My evidence was specious, at best. As any collector back then knew, the only real upside in baseball cards was in rookie cards. No one knew exactly why this was the case, except that it was usually harder to find rookie cards of players because, when guys were rookies, they weren't likely to be in All-Star sets or special-feature team cards. But it wasn't my responsibility to provide Clint with the cons of the swap. I had proposed a trade, and it was up to him to decide whether to give it a Yay, a Nay, or a Go Fuck Yourself.

"Come on, man. It's a good deal!"

This bit of exhortative support came from Max Phalen, whose hair was now less white-blonde and more regular-blonde, but who still had the best laugh at Jefferson West, egging Clint on. Baseball card trading is like boxing: no one came to watch the two ogres retreat to their corners.

"Shut up, butthole!"

This was Clint's response—a response that meant I had him right where I wanted him. He was agitated; he didn't want to back down.

"Fine," he said.

I took a deep breath to prevent my hands from shaking as I took the Griffey cards out of their plastic homes and handed them to Clint. He in turn passed me the Clemens rookie card, which I slipped into a free slot at the back of my collection.

I'd finally done it; I'd gotten revenge on Clint Byrd.

At school after the trade, I felt like Bilbo Baggins, giddy about a thing I possessed—a thing whose significance was known only to me. Not even another Language Arts class during which Lisa Zerr paid only cursory attention to my *Doogie Howser*-related witticisms could get me down.

On the first segment of my ride home—from Ozawkie to Meriden—I kept my binder shut. There would be no more trades this day, at least not by me. Then, on the trip from Meriden to home, I looked at my precious Roger Clemens card four times, each time hardly believing that I'd pulled off such a blockbuster.

After supper, I gathered my brothers in my room and took the Clemens card out of its plastic encasement, explaining the deal I'd made but leaving out the part about the tokens. I would take that part to the grave.

Then, as I was telling my brother Dan to BE CAREFUL, our mother knocked on the door to my room.

"Paul?" she said, sticking her head through the crack formed when she pushed the door over the blue carpet in my room. I didn't like the edge I heard in her voice.

"Yeah?"

"Did you trade some baseball cards with Clint Byrd today?"

"Yeaaaaah. Why?"

"His mother is on the phone. And she says you ripped him off."

Goddammit, Clint.

"What do you mean? We made a trade, fair and square."

"That's not what his mother is saying."

"What does she know about baseball cards?"

My mother frowned.

"I want you to apologize to Clint."

I could handle that. I mean, what kind of pissant tells his mother about a trade that he doesn't think is fair? But still, no big deal-

"And I want you to give him the card back."

Oh, for the love of Will Clark.

"But Mom-"

"Paul, you shouldn't take advantage of people."

Tell that to Clint the Thief, I wanted to say.

"I wasn't...taking advantage of him. Those Griffey cards-"

She fixed her stare on me.

"You know what I mean."

The next day, I undid the trade with Clint. I was furious, of course, that a chance at revenge had slipped through my fingers. Not that I could admit it; what kind of seventh grader still cared that he hadn't gotten the clock radio he'd wanted? Of course, that was why the baseball card fleecing had been so perfect. It was self-contained, elegant, tit-for-tat. Like Clint with my tokens, I'd bided my time, waiting for just the right moment. It had arrived and I'd executed my plan, and on a far greater scale: that Roger Clemens rookie card that was going to be worth hundreds of dollars someday! Maybe thousands! The *Beckett*s my brothers and I thumbed through at the Topeka Food4Less implied as much; cards' values were only continuing to skyrocket.

But that was all gone now.

And so it might seem like I was going to learn the lesson most of us learn, which is that life is not like *The Princess Bride*. True revenge (like true love) is a rare beast indeed, and most of the time, the best you're going to get is far less than what you'd hoped for.

But then, in the mid-nineties, the bottom fell out of the baseball card market after it became clear that every other father had given their sons the same advice mine had, which was to hold onto their cards because "someday, those things might be worth something."

And then, of course, Roger Clemens was implicated in the steroid scandals of the late 1990s and early 2000s, becoming, in fact, the poster boy for cheating.

Accordingly, one can now buy that Roger Clemens rookie card on eBay at the Buy It Now price of $24.99.

Or about a dollar less than what it was worth when I made the trade.

You'll meet another girl.
You'll get another chance on another basketball team.
What now seems irreplaceable probably is not.
Everything will be OK.

These are the things I tell myself as Chan Marshall finishes "The Moon."

And as I finish the last Oatmeal Creme Pie in the brown paper bag.

BARCELONA, SPAIN

A Wednesday morning

When I see her from across the concourse, I am amazed, again, at how pretty she is. Green eyes, silvery blond hair, everything else in its place.

So pretty that, when I first saw her a week before this, standing in front of a red Ferrari in the main terminal of the Barcelona airport, the only thing that flashed across my brain was:

Oh shit oh shit oh shit oh shit oh shit oh shit oh shit oh shit

She was everything I'd ever imagined, whenever I'd imagined whom I'd end up with when my basketball career was over. And then, after curse words stopped scrolling across my brain and I got up the courage to walk over and deliver the best line I could come up with, which was to ask her if she spoke English, she turned out to be interesting. And funny. And smart; she spoke four languages, including the one nearest and dearest to my simple American tongue.

She told me her job was to offer passersby a photo with herself and another tall blond girl in front of the Ferrari. Anyone who got their picture taken was entitled to 20% off at the store behind them, which sold Ferrari watches and jackets to people who can't afford Ferrari cars.

After twenty minutes, I asked for her number, telling her I needed to do some work, when the truth was that I felt like I needed to get out while I was on top.

She considered my request just long enough for me to think she was being coy.

Then she said no.

I took it like a shotgun blast to the chest, mumbling a polite, "Nice to meet you," as I staggered away. I found a spot near an outlet and plugged in my computer, determined to lick the ghastly wound with social media and Kansas City Royals box scores. But after an hour of pretending to be interested in the screen in front of me, I walked back to her spot in front of the Ferrari store and told her I couldn't help but think there was some connection between us.

Hope springs eternal with love at first sight.

I handed her the note I'd composed, written on a page I'd torn out of the tiny atlas I carried around in my backpack. It was the page for Kansas, of course, and the note said that this was my home state and that it had been nice to meet her and I hoped I could show it to her someday. And here was my email address.

She smiled then. And said she'd email me.

And she did!

And that's why this time, eight days after that first meeting, I'm familiar. Or as familiar as a person can be after one hour-long conversation and five emails.

She is not, though, expecting the crutches, which is why when she sees *me* she puts a hand to a cheek and her mouth forms the familiar syllables: "Oh. My. God."

I stop because I'm exhausted already, and I'm only halfway across the concourse, in front of a store that sells duty-free watches and travel pillows.

I flash her what I hope will be interpreted as a rueful grin and then resume my laborious walk over to her.

When I arrive in front of her there is an exclamation point after the "Hi" I say.

Her hands are still on her cheeks.

She looks down at my crutches.

Then up at me.

9

Failure

I first played basketball in Spain during my second year as a pro. After the expiration of a 10-day contract with the Atlanta Hawks, I signed on to join perennial Barcelona-based power Joventut as a replacement for a fellow journeyman who'd fallen out of favor with the team. That time, I was in Spain for four months. My brother Dan came to live with me. I dated a very short German girl who sometimes cried after sex. I traveled to Slovenia on a plane so small and fragile that our biggest players had to sit in the front to keep it from tipping over backward.

Joventut finished fifth (out of eighteen teams), earning it the spot in the playoffs I'd flown across the Atlantic to produce.

I went to Spain a second time, not to help a team into the playoffs but to assist with catastrophe-avoidance. A team on the Balearic island of Menorca had called my agent with eight weeks left in their season, hoping I was the player they needed to help pull them out of last place.

In the ACB (*Asociación de Clubs Baloncesto*), the Spanish first division, the teams that finish in the last two spots in the standings are demoted to the second division. This usually seems odd to Americans who can't imagine sending, say, the San Francisco Giants to baseball's AAA level, but it's more normal than not. Almost all European leagues, including soccer, work this way.

When the Menorcan team called, I was just arriving back into something like basketball shape. After getting dropped like a bag of hammers by the Timberwolves, my *right* knee had begun to click, pop, and ache anytime I did anything more than walk briskly, a lot like my *left* knee had done that summer.

I drove to Iowa again, to see the same orthopedist (who was unexpectedly becoming a recurring character in my adult life) and to have my right knee sliced open a couple of months before my 29th birthday.

Another, less-orthopedically-detailed way of putting all of that would be: the window on my moneymaking years as a basketball player wasn't necessarily closing, but someone in the room was definitely saying, "It's getting a little cold in here, innit?"

So, when the team in Menorca offered me $50,000 to play eight weeks of basketball, I signed the contract as fast as my fingers could form my name in cursive.

Menorca is the least famous of Spain's Mediterranean islands, trailing Ibiza, which is known as a destination for models, reality stars and amateur cocaine dealers, and Mallorca, which houses a million people, a population that swells significantly in the summer, when German and British tourists arrive to pinken their skin.

Curiously, though, Menorca was the only Balearic island with a team in the ACB. That team, called ViveMenorca, had clambered into the ACB thanks to a combination of pluck and luck—pluck and luck that had, it seemed, run out in time for the team's first season in the top league. ViveMenorca had won only seven of the twenty-six games it had played that season. My job, I was told, was to help us win at least five, and maybe six, of the final eight games.

My efforts at salvation did not get off to an auspicious start. We lost my first game at the home court of league leader FC Barcelona. But as I adjusted to an island in the Mediterranean whose climate was more like that of an island in the North Sea, we started rattling off wins. Two at home and then a big one on the road against ACB stalwart Unicaja Malaga. It was enough to move us out of last place.

After the win in Malaga, we hamstrung our progress with a home loss in front of a sold-out crowd of 5,500, which represented almost exactly 1/11th of the island's total population. But we recovered and won our next two games, setting the stage for a showdown on the season's last weekend—a showdown that would determine whether my time in Menorca would be declared a success.

There were two ways for us to escape the clutches of the second division. We could beat the team from Murcia, which was also fighting to avoid demotion. Or, if a team called Valladolid (because it was in Valladolid) beat the team called Alicante (because it was in Alicante) in a game that would be played at the same time as ours, both participants in our game—Murcia and ViveMenorca—would play in the ACB the next season.

In order to make sure we understood fully the stakes at hand, our team's president told us that if we kept the team in the first division, he'd pay each of us 10,000 Euros (about $13,000, at the time). My teammates were thrilled with this development. I, on the other hand, was oddly ambivalent when I heard the news. This ambivalence could not be attributed to any kind of disdain for the sum of money involved; I wanted an extra $13,000 like anyone wants an extra $13,000. Nor was the problem that I didn't care about winning the game. I wanted to win very badly; I just had a different motivation. Specifically, the identity of a particular American the Murcian team had signed two weeks after my own arrival in Spain: my college teammate, Marcus Fizer.

Since being selected fourth in the NBA draft after leading us to that fateful game against Michigan State in the NCAA Elite Eight, Marcus's pro career hadn't gone quite as he'd planned. After four middling seasons with the Chicago Bulls, his coaches had grown tired of his general unpredictability, and he'd been left in similar straits to mine: playing in Spain for whatever money we could get.

In some parallel universe, I might have felt something like camaraderie with Marcus; here we were, far from home, playing in a game that neither of us could ever have expected to play. But I'd disliked Fizer since the day I'd met him on his official visit to Iowa State, and he'd pointed out how dumb it looked when I walked with my hands in my jean pockets. Since then, resentment had churned inside me whenever he was around. Some of this resentment was justified: he got the headlines and the accolades while the rest of us toiled away in semi-anonymity, beholden to his whims. One fall, he'd threatened to quit and had subsequently been excused from preseason conditioning for a month. But my resentment of Marcus wasn't entirely logical. I was also scared of him, probably because Marcus managed to touch on most of the various inferiority complexes I'd ever bred in myself. I'd always thought of myself as too skinny; Marcus was so muscle-bound that he looked like he'd been sketched by Stan Lee. I'd never been as confident as I'd liked; Marcus gave off the aura of someone who'd tear your face off if the mood struck him.

So, yeah, I didn't much care about the $13,000. I needed to beat Marcus Fizer.

Fitting with the dramatic nature of the set-up, ViveMenorca v. Murcia didn't start out so well for my team. We played the first half like we'd been dosed with tranquilizers and at halftime were down by three touchdowns, which is a joke that will only land if you like mixed sports metaphors.

Standing at the dry erase board and contemplating what to say, our coach looked at us with disdain as he tried to decide if he should scream at us or shake his head and give up.

"*Que pasa con Valladolid?*" he asked the back of the room.

"*Abajo,*" our trainer said. "*Por ocho.*"

Valladolid, the team we needed to win in case we didn't, was down by eight points. And Valladolid wasn't good; it didn't seem likely that they would mount a comeback. Thus, our collective fate was tied to our ability to get our shit together, which might have been what our coach said when he was screaming at us in Spanish at the end of halftime.

To be fair, he also might have been ordering us to bring him ice cream after the game. My ability to understand Spanish decreased with each decibel at which it was delivered.

In the second half, our coach put into the game the lineup that had been the most successful since I'd arrived on the island: our two Croatian wing players, our Bosnian point guard, the other American, and me. Any reluctance to use this lineup could be chalked up to a reasonable bit of xenophobia; the Spanish league, like most European leagues, wants its teams to promote the play of Spanish players. The league knows that fans like watching players who look like they do, except taller.

Thanks to the go-for-broke attitude the five of us had developed whenever we'd been allowed to play together, we clawed back into the game against Murcia, and at the end of the third quarter we were down only 12. Midway through the fourth: the deficit was only six. And then, with 30 seconds left, on a jump shot by one of our Croatians, we took a one-point lead. The Murcian crowd sat in stunned silence as the Croatian galloped down the court, pounding his chest. In the timeout that followed, our head coach asked me if I wanted to guard the player everyone in the gym knew would get the ball: Marcus Fizer.

The truth was that I didn't *want* to guard Marcus. What I *wanted* to do was lie on a couch and watch *Seinfeld* re-runs. But I also knew that I would never let myself live it down if I didn't "step up" or "rise to the challenge" or any of the other dumb platitudes athletes and their commentators use. If I could stop Marcus I would lay to rest some demons that had haunted the outer reaches of my psyche for around a decade. Plus, I'd make an extra $13,000 and resuscitate a career that I'd begun to think might be dead on the table.

So I nodded and my teammates and I stood up from the huddle, knowing we had only to make one last defensive stand and the game would be over.

After taking the post-timeout inbounds pass, Marcus coolly dribbled the ball up the court as I shadowed his zig-zaggy path. As we crossed half court, I saw in Marcus's eyes a familiar sight—a sight I was afraid I'd see. Fury, plain and simple. This fury was what had always made Marcus a dangerous (and effective) basketball player. Once, he'd left one of our preseason pick-up games to find a chair in the hallway which, upon his return to the gym, he'd brandished over his head while walking toward our New Zealand-born center who, evidently, had done something Marcus didn't like. The next year, during a practice inside Hilton Coliseum, Marcus had body-slammed me into the basket's support, using only the ball we'd both been tussling over as leverage, and of which I wouldn't let go.

And now that fury was back.

We arrived at the spot where the play would start: thirty feet from the basket we were defending, on the side of the court opposite our bench. I watched Marcus's eyes as they stayed fixed on the shot clock. He was waiting for it to count down to the appropriate number of seconds, in order to leave us with as little time as possible to retaliate, if and when he scored. I licked my hands and ran them over the bottoms of my shoes, hoping the spit might give me just the bit of traction I needed. Then Marcus made his move. Squinting in the way I'd seen so many times, he looked down at my feet and his dribbling went from time-killing to Paul-killing. He went right and I kept my shoes moving, which is harder than you might think; I'd played the entire second half AND I'd had two knee surgeries in the preceding nine months.

Next, Marcus went left, back toward the middle of the court. I stayed in front of him, thinking primarily of the shot clock I knew was ticking away and secondarily about how surreal this was, that I was here and Marcus was here, and our basketball fates were tied to a moment that would be unbelievable, were someone to write it as fiction.

Then we went right again, and I told myself to keep my feet moving, to stay activ-

WHAMMO!

Impact on the right side of my body.

Marcus was receiving a screen—one of his teammates blocking me from his path—and I had to call for a switch, leaving Marcus to my fellow American, Chris, an undersized center from the University of West Virginia.

I watched breathless, as Marcus went to work on Chris, who knew far less than I did about Marcus's tendencies.

As I searched for someone to keep out of the lane, Marcus picked up his dribble, as we say in basketball-speak. I watched him give Chris a fake. I watched Chris rise in the air. I watched Marcus lean into Chris. I heard a whistle. I heard Chris say, "Fuck!"

I heard myself echo him.

Chris had fouled Marcus, who walked to the free throw line as my team huddled in the middle of the free throw lane, seeking refuge from 12,000 screaming Murcian fans. I calmed my frantic teammates (players from the ex-Yugoslavia have a tendency toward volatility) and pointed out the good news: we still had seven seconds to work with.

After going over a plan that could only generously be labeled a half-baked one, we retreated to our positions on the lane, where we watched as Marcus, his face a calm mask, made the first free throw—because that's the sort of thing players like Marcus do. Then we watched him make the second free throw—because that's also the sort of thing players like Marcus do.

We were down one point. We were out of timeouts. But we had those seven seconds. Which was far better than no seconds.

After the ball dropped through the net, I carried it to the requisite spot behind the out-of-bounds line and threw it to our Bosnian point guard, a 5'11" fireball with spiky hair like Oliver Bledsoe, who'd bailed us out of at least two games with last-second three-pointers.

I aimed my weary legs downcourt, headed for a position at the top of the key on the other end, where I'd be ready to shoot a three-pointer in case the Bosnian passed the ball my way. As I arrived at my prescribed position, I could tell that such specific heroism wasn't a likely outcome. The Bosnian was preparing himself for a shot. So, I did the next best thing to a three-pointer: I started for the basket to put myself in position for an offensive rebound.

As I slipped down the lane, dodging Marcus and his Murcian teammates, all of whom who were trying to keep me from my desired spot near the basket, I watched out of the corner of my eye as the Bosnian, sure enough, rose for his shot—a shot that I could tell, as soon it left his hand, was bound to come up short.

Way short.

Air-ball short.

I hadn't provided for this contingency when I left the top of the key. To catch the ball, I would have to perform an all-engines-stop to keep my 230-pound body from rocketing out of bounds. But I had to help us win this game. I had to save my team and my career. I had to beat Marcus.

I planted my left foot and somehow, someway, I caught the ball around my hip, in one of those strange, last-second stabs that happens when an object ends up in a spot where you didn't expect it to be.

Then, a few things happened almost simultaneously.

First, I recognized that the buzzer signifying the game's end had not sounded, meaning I still had time to get the ball up and into the basket.

Second, I began to retard the ball's downward progress, probably with my adductor muscles and hip flexor, in order to twist my body, which was now almost entirely under the basket, and toss the ball back up toward the basket.

And third, my left ankle shattered.

Here is what happens when you have just caught a basketball while all of your considerable weight is being supported by a talus bone that has just snapped: you crumple to the floor, the ball bounces harmlessly away, the buzzer sounds, and the home team's supporters rush the court like someone there is throwing money into the air. You realize you have lost, Marcus Fizer has won, and this ankle thing—this can't be good for your hopes of a continued basketball career, not with it feeling like Kathy Bates has just made its acquaintance with her sledge.

And then, because you are the sort of person who cries when things appear to be hopeless, you start crying.

Through my tears, I saw my American teammate, Chris, walking toward me, picking his way through Murcian fans who were pouring onto the court to celebrate their team's salvation. He was untucking his jersey, like he always did after games. When he got to me, he asked if I was OK. I shook my head and pointed at my ankle just as a fan leapt over my leg.

"I don't think so," I said.

"Jesus," he said. Then he cracked half a smile.

"What could you possibly be smiling about?" I asked him.

"Valladolid came back. They beat Alicante."

In all the fourth-quarter madness, I'd forgotten that there was another path to salvation for my team. A path we had inadvertently stumbled upon, like conquistadors from the very country I was in, hacking their way across the Yucatan.

Valladolid had rallied. We were saved. ViveMenorca would play the next season in the ACB.

I was given a set of crutches to help me get back to Menorca, where a crowd was waiting at the airport to celebrate our salvation. Two days later, I would use the same crutches to pick my way up a set of stairs that took my teammates and me to a platform in front of the main square in Mahon, Menorca, where 5,000 people turned out to listen to us give speeches celebrating our tie for 16th place.

When I got home, there was an email from the girl from the airport. She was still working the Ferrari job. I was connecting through Barcelona on my way home.

We made a plan to meet.

"Wait," she says, a glimmer in her green eyes. "You broke your ankle for nothing?"

In the course of the telling of the story, we have moved to a circular café that sits like an island in the stream of passengers on their ways to a thousand possible places. I take a sip from the tea I ordered.

I grin. She's right, kind of.

But also, not at all.

In twenty minutes, I will leave the Barcelona airport with a funny feeling in my stomach—a feeling I will tell her about, when I am at home, in the house whose down payment was provided for by my first trip to Spain, propped in front of my computer and sending her an email. I will say that even though I've only met her twice, it feels like I've known her forever.

She will say the same thing.

I will return to Menorca the following season. I will have my first ankle surgery there. I will lose something like $70,000 because of this ankle surgery. My team will not be much better than it was the year before; the season will, again, come down to the last game of the year.

But during that season, I will sneak away from the island to have a first date with the girl from the airport. She will surprise me in Menorca one Sunday morning. I will bake her a birthday cake and carry it to her on my lap in an airplane.

When I leave Menorca that next year, we will move in together in Barcelona, in a part of the city called L'Eixample. She will teach me how to speak Spanish without an accent. I will show her Kansas, just like I said I would.

She will spend Thanksgiving at my parents' house. My mother will be afraid that I will move to Europe forever.

Thanks to our win in Malaga, I will be offered a short-term contract with that team. I will take that job. She will come with me. (The girl, not my mother.)

It will be the last professional basketball team I play for.

She will break up with me soon after.

I will be heartbroken.

Especially when I find out she's dating a guy from Barcelona I thought was my friend.

When it is over, I will have learned small things like how

to dress like a grown-up, how to eat olives, and what to say after you ask someone for directions in Spain. (*Muy amable.*)

I will have learned some bigger things, too.

The value of walking up to someone without a plan for what you'll say.

The beauty of waking up next to someone, day after day.

The agony of letting someone go.

So, no, it will not be for nothing that I have broken my ankle.

Even though we don't know that yet.

KANSAS CITY

A Saturday night

I'm standing at the only sink in the cramped bathroom that's upstairs at my favorite bar in Kansas City, a place where the staff wears black ties with silver clips, the bar is rimmed with brass, and no one ever asks me how tall I am. Downstairs, at one of the dark wooden tables where I've spent too many nights trying to keep out the cold, there's a girl I think I might like. And whom I think might like me.

But I need to get her alone to find out.

Problem is, she's with two guys from her band and they're talking about going back to the hotel, and if that happens I can't imagine she'll be able to get away from them even if she wanted to. They aren't her older brothers, but they sure act like it.

Then an idea hits me.

My hand shakes as I pull my phone out of my pocket. You could say there's no rush, but you'd be wrong. It's midnight and they'll be back in Brooklyn tomorrow. Plus I've already been in the bathroom for a couple of minutes and there's nothing less romantic than her thinking I've been up here pooping.

I type,

> Do you want to get a drink with me –
> just me – now?

I press Send and put the phone in my pocket, turning to the mirror. As I wash my hands, I blow out my cheeks and grin, not sure how I got here and even less sure what I'll do when I get downstairs. Because what if I get down there and she hasn't read the message? I'll have to ask her if she got it and, Jesus, that'll be awkward.

I feel the vibration all down my right leg.

I reach for a paper towel, pretending to be nonchalant for as long as it takes to dry my hands. Then I dig for my phone like it's the gold flake that's going to pay for this winter's coal.

I close one eye as I open it, wincing.

> Sure

My shoulders slump in relief and I smile for the benefit of the mirror.

Downstairs, she has to break the news to her bandmates. "Uh, yeah, guys," she says, jerking a thumb at me. "I'm gonna go with him."

"Oh, OK," one of them says.

They're appraising me differently now. I've just changed from potential friend to potential Yoko. But we're all adults here and anyway, one of the benefits of being 6'9" is that people think you're intimidating.

I shake their hands and she and I push through the bar's stubborn door and we go next door, to a different bar that's no longer called what it was then. There, we sit for two hours in front of the array of colorful bottles on the wall, drinking beer and mining away until we hit a vein.

"Yes!" she exclaims. "I know exactly what you mean!"

I've been telling her how difficult my life is to explain to people who haven't been part of that life for very long. She understands, she says, because being in a rock band is a lot like being a professional basketball player. It seems a lot more glamorous than it is, especially to outsiders who can't understand that yes, traveling is illuminative and formative, but getting up at 3:45 to catch a bus to the airport is not. Especially when you can't remember what city you're in.

We dig deeper, and it seems like we're on sufficiently solid rock that I can admit that I'm a little mixed-up now that basketball is over. I tell her I've been seeing a therapist in order to deal with the end of the only profession I've known. My psychologist says it's like I've been through a divorce, or like I'm a 65-year-old man who's been put out to pasture at State Farm.

Either way, it's going to take a while.

She nods as she looks at the mirror.

"I get it. Because, for us, it's hard to do this sort of thing without it becoming your entire life."

I want to hug her, because this is what I'm discovering about myself in my therapist's office: that I screwed up somewhere along the way. While everyone else was learning that they were worthwhile whether they were good at their jobs or not, I kept attaching my self-worth to my ability to a play a game that was bound to let me down, physiologically and chronologically.

We stare into our drinks and I wonder if she has a boyfriend. I haven't asked, because I am trying my best to stay in the moment—something I'm learning about thanks to meditation and a man named Jon Kabat-Zinn.

But moments add up whether we like it or not and pretty soon, the bar is closing and we're on the street in the dark.

Her hotel isn't far, so I tell her I'll walk her.

I'm wondering if she'll invite me up, but when we get to the parking lot it becomes clear that this will be no wild, sex-fueled first night. Her band's appearance in Kansas City isn't exactly Zeppelin at Shea Stadium. They're two to a room at a hotel that straddles the line dividing boutique and Super 8, leaving us in the parking lot hemming and hawing like one of us is trying to buy a used car.

It's such a stereotype, too: end of the night, standing outside her hotel, not drunk, but a few drinks in. It's too obvious, too predictable. *Plus,* my brain says. *You might see her again. It'd be cool to have her as a friend.*

But then my brain says something else.

I bend down. I lean toward her. I kiss her.

And.

She kisses me back.

It is lovely, our kiss. Not because it is a great kiss because what first kiss is?

No, it is lovely because it is unexpected; because when we got up today neither of us had an inkling that this is how our day would end. Or at least, not much inkling. I'd be a liar if the thought hadn't crossed my mind.

When we are done, we have that little hug that post-kiss humans do.

Then she says, "How did you know to do that?"

10

In a Hundred Years, It Isn't Going to Matter Anyway

A middle school crush is like the Wave at a baseball game. You can tell the direction it's headed. You might even be able to guess how long it'll last. But who knows what combination of factors caused some guy in Section 29 to put down his beer, throw up his hands, and get the thing going.

My Wave started in seventh grade, around the time I was assigned a desk behind Lisa Zerr in Language Arts. Lisa was eminently crushable thanks to her shiny brown hair, her rapidly developing breasts, and her palpable disdain for authority, which manifested in the names of rock bands she'd scrawled on her plain, blue notebook—a far cry from the Trapper Keepers the rest of us conformists toted through the halls.

But what I most liked about Lisa was simpler than any of that. I liked her face. Just looking at it made me feel like everything I was worried about—which consisted chiefly of the Kansas City Royals' playoff drought, what had happened at the end of *Where the Red Fern Grows*, and the occasional prepubescent existential crisis—would work out OK.

I was desperate for a way to get Lisa to turn that face my way more often. But everything I thought of seemed bogus, the sort of question that would mark me a king-sized dweeb. I couldn't ask her who the bands were; everybody else probably knew who Warrant was. And it didn't seem like a great idea to bring up how rad I thought Lisa looked in her red-and-black cheerleading outfit; that seemed a little creepy.

Then, one Thursday, Max Phalen and I were singing the praises of a certain sitcom about a certain kid doctor.

Lisa whirled in her desk.

"You like *Doogie Howser*?"

"Uh, yeah?"

"Me too!"

As I basked in the full force of Lisa's smile, I mentally apologized to Max. I'd just found a new Ebert.

Pretty soon, Lisa got into the habit of turning around to talk to me every day before Language Arts, even on non-Thursdays. I was getting used to the routine, the banter, the way I felt when she looked at me (like I'd just doubled down the line in Little League).

And then it happened.

She touched my arm.

My Wave had just made a full circuit of the stadium.

There was one problem: I didn't know how to keep it going. Then, along came a middle school dance and I thought I was saved.

It was never clear who put up the posters for our middle school dances. The secretaries? The cheerleaders? Overzealous parents? It was a mystery that confounded me as thoroughly as any conversation with Lisa Zerr that didn't involve Doogie Howser.

What was not a mystery was how the music would be supplied.

BRING YOUR TAPES! the posters said.

There was no specific set of guidelines regarding what was allowed and what was not. While anything by Eazy-E was frowned upon, our principal Mr. Neilsen (who doubled as the DJ) took a remarkably laissez-faire attitude toward the playlists. The Eighties had just ended, so there were plenty of tunes by the likes of Madonna, George Michael, and Prince. Plus "hair metal" and its ubiquitous power ballads. Poison's "Every Rose Has Its Thorn," Mötley Crüe's "Without You" and White Lion's "When the Children Cry"—these all figured heavily in the mix.

I didn't own any cassettes; my exposure to music consisted of whatever I could hear out of the clock radio I'd gotten for Christmas two years before. (Which, thanks to Clint Byrd, was exactly two years after I *should* have had a clock radio.) So my preparation for my first-ever dance consisted of putting on the navy blue chamois shirt my mother had bought on sale at JC Penney, tucking it into my tan Dockers, and riding to Ozawkie where, after we parked in the drop-off circle in front of the school, my father turned to me in the Grand Voyager and asked me who I wanted to dance with.

My response was something between a murmur and a mumble. I wasn't used to my father asking me about my personal life. Mostly, I knew my father as someone who yelled at me about buckets—not stepping in them when I was swinging a baseball bat, and trying to look like a man when they were full of water and I was transporting them to our chickens.

"OK," he said. "Whoever it is, just ask."

I took a breath while I tried to process this new side of my father.

"But what if she says no?"

He smiled then, his graying mustache straightening over his lip.

"Who cares? In a hundred years, it isn't going to matter anyway."

I nodded as I thought about the wisdom he'd just dispensed.

It made a lot of sense, when you thought about it. In a hundred years, I was going to be dead, Lisa was going to be dead, even Nikki Sixx was going to be dead. So what did it matter if Lisa shut me down harder than Public Enemy?

"OK," I said, flashing my dad what I hoped was a confident smile. "I'll try."

Inside the darkened music room where my classmates were milling around, I immediately regretted my entire wardrobe. It was clear that my friends' ensembles were far cooler than mine. I mean, Darin Densmore had a shirt made of silk!

Darin brought another asset to the dance floor: he wasn't terrified of our female counterparts. This didn't make Darin unique. Oliver Bledsoe had hit puberty around the same time as Darin (about three years before me). The difference between the two was that Darin didn't make fun of me about this hormonal discrepancy, which was why Darin had become my new Best Friend of Record. Also, Darin played trombone, like I did. But this fact—that Darin and I were rapidly becoming so close that when he left for college in August after our senior year I would break down and cry—did not mean he was going to be at my side throughout this middle school dance.

He had rugs to cut.

I took one of the chairs that ringed the room. It wasn't long before my fellow wallflowers joined me. Max Phalen, wearing a rugby shirt with horizontal stripes in green, yellow, and red, as if he was supporting the soccer team from Ghana. Then Clint Byrd, his clothes lined up with mine on the cool spectrum. (We'd made up since the baseball card trade, Clint and me. Dorks like us needed as many allies as we could get.)

Meanwhile, Lisa Zerr was a thousand miles away, sitting and laughing with her friends on the other side of the dance floor. And I couldn't imagine how I would close the gap—how I could get that Wave going again.

But then, after three songs that left the dance floor looking like a hand grenade had just gone off, I caught a break: the "Snowball" dance. Whenever Mr. Neilsen paused the song and said, "Snowball!" into the microphone inside his makeshift DJ booth, everyone had to switch partners. If there were still kids on the sidelines, you had to ask one of them. This meant it was inevitable that A) someone would ask me and that B) I would subsequently *have* to ask someone else.

It was almost too easy.

Almost.

Because, even after being armed with this godsend, I still couldn't muster the chutzpah to ask Lisa Zerr to dance—couldn't remember my father's surprising wisdom about how, in a hundred years, it wasn't going to matter anyway.

So instead, I relegated myself to the second and third tier of my female classmates: your Erin Turkelsons, your Hannah Smyths, your Sheila Joneses. Then I went back and sat down with Max and Clint, ignored by everyone.

Well, almost everyone.

When I was seven, in one of my mother's many efforts to make sure I became Well-Rounded, she'd enrolled me in a square-dancing club. The other boys and I wore Western suits; the girls wore poufy dresses in sky blue or marigold yellow. We practiced in the Methodist church basement, learning our round-your-pardners and our do-si-dos to a level of proficiency that, in high school, when our forward-thinking gym teacher organized a unit on dancing, I had to make an effort to actively forget half of what I knew to avoid running the risk of being marked as the dork who knew how to square dance.

We were assigned partners at one of the first square dance meetings-slash-practice sessions. Mine had been Nancy Smolinski.

It was probably this sense of shared connection that caused Nancy to feel possessive anytime music started playing and bodies started moving. Either that or the fact that, truth be told, I'd been a damn good square-dancer.

Somewhere near the punch bowl, 'round about the time Mr. Neilsen was cuing up a slow Steve Winwood song, Nancy threw her arms around me.

"It's my turn," she whispered into my ear, as if people were waiting in line for the honor. I probably would have gone for it, except for the look in her jet-black eyes. That look was terrifying—it promised a dance now, a blowjob in two years. (Not that I knew exactly what a blowjob was; I just had a feeling.)

Nancy lived with her mother in a trailer that was literally on the other side of the railroad tracks that ran to Meriden's grain Co-op. And while at Jefferson West this was hardly enough to make anyone think twice—half my friends lived in trailers or might as well have—it was just enough to make her seem like trouble to me.

So I told her I had to go to the bathroom.

On my way out of the music room I noted a strange combination of exhilaration and relief. The former because someone liked me. The latter because I'd gotten away!

I didn't have to go to the bathroom, of course, and this wouldn't have been a problem if the middle school bathroom had been a normal bathroom: urinal, wall, urinal, a few stalls with toilets. But our middle school bathroom wasn't a normal bathroom. I mean, it got off to a reasonable start: the urinals were floor-length models, the sort that should be *de rigueur* in every men's room in the world. But after that, things took an unacceptable turn: the toilets in the main bathroom at Jefferson West Middle weren't enclosed by doors. And even *that* would have been mildly excusable, if those toilets had at least been separated by walls. But that element of the design had eluded whomever had erected this particular pair of shitters, and so those toilets sat like griffons overlooking a mid-city plaza, daring someone to use them. And what was incomprehensible to shy little ol' me—someone who hadn't done real business in a school bathroom since an emergency clean-up in second grade, necessary when he'd accidentally pooped his pants while trying to fart when his bus had bounced over the one speed bump in the Greater Meriden Metropolitan Area—was that someone sat astride one of those steeds, raining assaults both physical and olfactory on the water below.

Specifically, Justin Bridges, sitting there with a grin like a watermelon.

"You watch that tape of your mom and dad lately?"

In other words, the bathroom wasn't the safe haven it might have been, and I did a lot of standing extremely close to that glorious floor-length urinal, pretending to pee before zipping up with a mock-satisfied sigh. I didn't need Justin Bridges knowing I was too scared to pee in front of him.

I didn't say anything as I moved to the sink, where I was going to continue my subterfuge with a thorough hand-washing.

As I turned off the faucet, Justin Bridges said, "Good luck with the ladies, PMS."

The irony in this sneering bit of faux-encouragement was that the first person I'd told my middle name was Lisa Zerr.

We'd been standing in the lunch line when she'd asked.

I'd been thrilled because middle names: that was, like, intimate!

"Oh," she said when I told her. "Murphy, that's cool. Irish, I guess."

My belly had gotten warm, then, because she was right. Murphy *was* Irish, which was a fact I thought only I'd known.

"Wait a second," said Oliver Bledsoe. "That means your initials are-"

And the rest was history. The news spread up and down the line like a prairie fire, explosions of laughter popping up every so often.

Had I known, by then, how to laugh at myself, I probably could have survived the fire. But I did not know, by then, how to laugh at myself. Plus, my initials' potential as a punch line had never occurred to me. I didn't completely understand what was so funny about PMS. I mean, I knew some of the girls in our classes were getting their periods. And I understood what a period was, conceptually. (Of course I did, with the mother I had.)

But pre-menstrual syndrome? That was well beyond my understanding of the English language and the acronyms it sprouts.

So I did the only thing I could do: I stood there with a wrinkled brow for several beats too long, right before I whipped out the only weapon I had in my arsenal: "Shut up, guys!"

That night, I asked my mother how she—a nurse!—could have made such an egregious nomenclatural oversight.

"Oh, honey," she said. "When you were born, they hadn't even coined the term!"

This, it turns out, was wildly inaccurate. The term "premenstrual syndrome" first appeared in medical literature in 1953, long before my birth in the late 1970s. But, I didn't exactly have Wikipedia dot org at my disposal, so my mother's explanation was enough to leave me feeling sufficiently reassured that I came to my own defense the next day, back in the lunch line.

"Guys! Remember how my initials stand for pre-menstrual syndrome? Well, they hadn't even made up that term when I was born, hahaha."

Oliver Bledsoe erupted in laughter.

"We don't care when they came up with the *term*! It's hilarious either way. And thanks for reminding us!"

So, instead of enduring one day of initials-based ridicule in the lunch line, I endured two. Plus whatever auxiliary opportunities presented themselves, like with Justin Bridges in the bathroom.

I gave Justin a half wave over my shoulder. And then it was back into the maw of the dance, to dodge Nancy Smolinski once more, and to hope Lisa Zerr stumbled into my arms.

But alas, at that first dance, I got no closer to Lisa Zerr than a glance from somewhere near the shelves that stored the tubas.

No matter, though. Before long, other social outlets were blooming like the heads on a hydra. There were garage birthday parties, which turned into dances. There were church parties, which also turned into dances. There was more dancing going on in Meriden, Kansas, in 1990 than there was in Elmore City, Oklahoma, in 1978.

The point, though, is this: I still had a chance to make my father proud—to make my move on Lisa Zerr.

Church-sponsored dances were usually held on Friday nights after high school football games. Theoretically this was a good idea; it gave us somewhere to go on a Friday. As long as we were inside the church, it didn't matter if half of us had tiny boners in our slacks. At least we were IN the church and, therefore, closer to God. (And away from the brake fluid fumes we could have been sniffing, which is a thing people in rural towns in Kansas sometimes did. Still do, I'd wager.)

But in reality, the combination of the end of the school week, the nighttime, and the unreleased testosterone provoked by watching our high school heroes try to smash opposing high school heroes made for a Wild West atmosphere that, inevitably, resulted in some dramatic arc or another: a breakup, threats of a fight, a handsy makeout during Bon Jovi's "Bed of Roses."

I spent the week before our first-ever church dance trying to figure out how I could get Lisa Zerr to dance with me. I had thoroughly buddied up to Lisa by then, engaging naturally a pathetic methodology that almost every male will recognize: I was trying to use the Friend Shortcut. I brought up *Doogie Howser* whenever I could. I pretended I didn't like Language Arts. I calculated ways to bring the conversation back around to middle names because now that she knew mine, that was basically like she'd seen me naked.

But while I was getting good at finding common conversational ground for three minutes before Language Arts started, I didn't know how I might aim the discourse toward anything romantic, i.e., Lisa and me dancing together. This wasn't true just because I was a coward.

It was also true because of Layne Bayer.

Layne Bayer was Lisa Zerr's boyfriend. He was also—damn him—an all-around good guy. His family was one of the pillars of the Jefferson West community. His brother, one year older, was, like Layne, a better-than-average athlete and a better-than-average student and better-than-average-looking. Their parents were young and hip and had money, at least by Jefferson County standards.

Also, *I* thought Layne Bayer was the bee's knees. I didn't dare get between him and his girl.

Still, though, Lisa was so tan.

So, you going to the dance tonight? <- This was my opener, couched fastidiously for the previous fifteen minutes of Language Arts.

She smiled. <- This meant yes.

…. < - This is where I was nervous.

I think you should save a dance for me. <- This is what she said that nearly caused me to enter atrial fibrillation.

I think that's a great idea. <- This is what I said before I almost collapsed.

I'd been afraid the Wave was gone for good, dead somewhere in left field. But it looked like someone was thinking about starting it up again.

I went to the football game, which our high school heroes lost, continuing a trend that would last until Darin Densmore took over as quarterback a few years later. Afterward, my mother dropped me off at the Methodist Church with a promise to see me in a couple of hours, not unlike when she'd dropped me off for those square-dancing lessons. But just because it was my mother dropping off didn't mean I'd forgotten my dad's words—words I was finally ready to act on.

In a hundred years, it isn't going to matter anyway.

I nearly skipped down the steps I usually trod on Wednesday nights for Boy Scout meetings, ready for my reward.

Tonight was the night: I was going to dance with Lisa Zerr.

I did a quick circuit of the church basement which, thanks to a few streamers and a carefully chosen lighting scheme (they'd turned off most of them), looked far different than I was used to. Notably: there was no Boy Scout flag present.

I found Max and Clint and we got punch that we took to the chairs we'd commandeered. We made a tiny circle and set about making it look like we didn't care if we ever danced with anyone. At other dances, this would have been entirely a façade on my part. But this time the apathy I was attempting to exude was an accurate representation of my true feelings.

I didn't want to dance with Anyone.

I wanted to make sure I was available whenever Lisa offered delivery on her promise.

I sat for a song ("In the Air Tonight"), got up for more punch during another song ("You're the Inspiration"), sat for another song ("Livin' on a Prayer"), went to the bathroom during another ("Straight Up").

After an hour, I was worried. Lisa and Layne hadn't left each other's sides, showed no signs of doing so, and Lisa hadn't even looked my way. How was I going to get her away from Layne?

I'd danced with Erin Turkelson once, but that was very obviously JUST AS FRIENDS, so there was no way Lisa could be mad at me, was there? No, no, she just hadn't gotten to me yet.

Mike + the Mechanics.

Madonna.

More Bon Jovi.

I looked down at the Timex—not an Ironman, because my parents couldn't quite afford that—and got the bad news.

It was 10:30. We had only half an hour left.

Huey Lewis.

Bell Biv Devoe.

Starship.

I looked at my watch.

10:50

Then I heard it.

First, the opening strains of a piano, before:

Look into my eyes
And you will see
What. You. Mean. To. Me
Search your heart
Search your soul

Every dance needs a last song. By our sophomore year in high school, it was almost always Boyz II Men's "The End of The Road." By the time I was a senior, reflecting the change in attitudes of both my classmates and country music at the time, it was "The Dance" by Garth Brooks.

But in seventh grade, it was this one: from the soundtrack to the Kevin Costner semi-classic, *Robin Hood: Prince of Thieves*, Bryan Adams's "Everything I Do (I Do It For You)."

I stood, ready for the Wave to hit my section, ready to throw my arms up...and around Lisa. She'd tell Layne that, look, she had to go right now. Then her eyes would find mine, and we'd have the dance that had been promised not just earlier today, but from the moment we'd ever started chatting before Language Arts.

It would be the first of many dances, the first step of many steps toward...who knew, who cared?!

What mattered was that we were going to start, tonight!

I looked at Lisa. But Lisa wasn't looking at me. In fact, Lisa's eyes were shut tight, because Lisa and Layne Bayer were MAKING OUT.

Full-on FRENCH KISSING.

Lisa, seriously, you don't seem to understand.
I would fight for you,
I'd lie for you,
Walk the wire for you,
I'd di-

Well, OK, I probably wouldn't *die* for you; we're 13, after all.

The rest of our comrades made their way to the dance floor, preparing to "hold" (stand eight inches away from) their favorite partners. Darin Densmore and Keri Donald. Erin Turkelson and Oliver Bledsoe.

Even Nancy Smolinski was out there.

But not Lisa and Layne, sitting on orange plastic chairs approximately 15 feet away from me, still Hoovering away at one another's faces.

The Wave was done, finished off just a couple of sections over.

I looked down at the floor, squeezing my eyes shut so tightly that little golden stars formed.

How could I have been such an idiot? Of course Lisa Zerr didn't want to dance with me, not when she had Layne Bayer on her arm.

When I opened my eyes, I was still hunched over my knees, which gave me a good view of the watch on my wrist—the watch that had been reminding me of my failure all night—and I hit upon an idea.

While not an Ironman, my watch did have an alarm function AND a stopwatch function. I turned to Max Phalen, who'd also been passed over for a last dance, and looked down at my left hand, where my right hand was poised and ready.

He chuckled, so when Lisa and Layne leaned in for another makeout session, I hit Start. And so, Max and Clint and I spent all six minutes and thirty-four seconds of Bryan Adams's second-most-famous song timing the kisses between Lisa Zerr and Layne Bayer.

By Monday, I'd pretty much forgotten about Friday night. I mean, I hadn't forgotten about the ruination of my crush on Lisa Zerr. I'd just banished it to the part of mind reserved for painful memories of cleaning out the chicken house and that time I shit my pants on the bus in Meriden.

I went to Language Arts assuming it would be like most Mondays. Lisa and I would laugh about our weekends and I would stare longingly at her notebook, wondering what it would be like to be trusted with the knowledge of who in the hell those devilish-looking bands were.

But this Monday was different. Today, she was ignoring me, busying herself with vocab work she usually put off until the last possible second. Could she have found out about my timekeeping?

No way; we'd been pretty surreptitious. And who would have told her?

Then, finally, at a break, she leaned over my desk, her breasts straining at the Jane's Addiction T-shirt she was wearing.

How was your Friday night? <- This was her opener.

I shrugged. <- This is what I did instead of admitting the truth, which was: Terrible! I mean, come on, Lisa, a dance with you would have meant everything to me. Was it so much to ask for you to make good on the one promise you made me?

What was our best time? <- This is when my blood turned to ice.

What do you mean? <- This is what I said, even though I knew exactly what she meant. And even though she knew I knew exactly what she meant.

If I'd been someone else—someone who knew, well, ANYTHING about girls—I might have nonchalantly reported the truth, which was 54 seconds. But I was not that person. And even though I felt in my heart that what I'd done to Lisa was far less damaging than what she'd done to me, I was the one who felt guilty.

I was scared because I was still a little boy and Lisa Zerr was very nearly a woman, and now I'd made her mad.

Lisa shook her head, her brain already racing out in front of mine, just like it would do a few years later when she accelerated her progress through high school so she could go off to college a year early.

Then, saying nothing, she turned around and went back to her work.

We never went out or "went out" or dated, Lisa Zerr and me. We certainly never FRENCH KISSED. This wasn't true because I timed Lisa Zerr making out with Layne Bayer in the Meriden United Methodist Church basement.

It was true because I never did anything about my crush on Lisa Zerr.

Nancy Smolinski understood what my dad was trying to tell me when he dropped me off at that first middle school dance, deploying the best advice he'd ever given that didn't involve buckets or backboards.

It isn't enough to have the crush. You also have to do something about it. You have to take the plunge, make the leap, go for broke.

You have to ask the girl to dance.

Or, if it happens to be the case that you are a very slow learner and it takes a really long time for fatherly advice to sink in: you have to ask the girl from the band if she wants to get a drink, just the two of you, and you have to endure the awkward departure of the girl's band, and then you have to kiss the glamorous girl from the band in the unglamorous parking lot of her mid-glamorous hotel.

Why?

Well, because it is possible that the kiss in the parking lot will lead to the girl from the band becoming your girlfriend, despite the fact that she lives in Brooklyn and you live in Kansas City.

But mostly because:

In a hundred years, it isn't going to matter anyway.

SOMEWHERE EAST OF DENVER

A Monday afternoon

188

PAUL SHIRLEY

"Here's the problem," she says. Her tone means she's probably twisting a few strands of her hair with her left hand as she says it. But I'm driving, so for all I know she's over there throwing up Crip signs.

"Allllrighty then," I say, doing a Jim Carrey impression that she's said before isn't nearly as funny as I think it is, which is exactly why I've done it.

She slugs me in the shoulder. Then she's quiet for half a second before she says, "I'm not sure I care anymore."

"I don't care no more. No more. No more. No more. No more."

"Huh?"

I smile into the rearview mirror. Clearly, she doesn't know *Hello, I Must Be Going!* like I do.

"Not your style. You were too busy listening to Yaz or Slowdive or whatever."

She turns to me, taking her left hand out of her hair and putting it on my right hand, which is draped across the stick shift.

"Do you know what I mean, though?"

I glance over at her. Her hair isn't whipping around her head, because her window is only cracked. But there's movement. It causes her to brush that hair out of her brown eyes. I think of another song, the obvious one, but the cover by the Southern California alternative band Everclear, which I liked very much in college.

"Of course I do."

"Really? I mean, I guess with you and basketball it probably always felt important no matter what—the fans and the TV cameras and all that. But with this band of ours that nobody wants to watch anymore—what does it matter?"

"Well, do you care? About the band, I mean?"

She turns to face front where, outside, mountains are whipping past. We're driving east, toward Kansas City. Two nights ago, I watched her band play its last show on this tour. And possibly, of all time.

"Sure. Maybe. I don't know." Then she sighs. "But who cares, even if I do?"

11

When You Care Enough to Punch Someone in the Face

I can't be sure why I took to spelling like I did, but it probably had something to do with control. In the world of my childhood, colored by Dan Rather and the Star Wars Program and the Soviet Union and Iran-Contra and all those rockets in Beirut, "pneumonia" always started with a P.

Practice felt meditative, and special. Mom or Dad with a sheetful of words, sitting at my desk chair. And me on my twin bed, more or less reading the words back. Because that's what spelling was for me. Someone said a word. That word popped into the screen inside my brain. I read it back, letter by letter.

It was not a glamorous talent. In fact, it is probably a stretch to call spelling ability a "talent" at all. More like a mutation, really. If I'd been an X-Man, my name would have been Webster; my special ability neither levitation nor the ability to conjure up meteorological events, but a photographic memory that applied only to the spelling of English words.

This ability mutation of mine probably would have gone largely unnoticed except for whichever bored early American decided that people might find it entertaining if he (or she) pitted school-aged kids against one another in spelling contests.

From the *Jamestown (NY) Journal*, January 26, 1831 edition:

*A big spelling match is announced in Covington, Ohio,
at the High School, when the lad that stands longest on
the floor and spells the biggest words without scratching
his head is to receive a fine present.*

At Jefferson West Elementary, circa the mid-1980s, there
were two separate spelling matches: one for first through third
grade, and one for fourth and fifth. Together, the two sessions
took up an entire morning in the gym, so all P.E. classes were
canceled for the day. Before the bees started, the student body
shuffled into the bleachers to watch the representatives from
their respective classes as they filed, one at a time, from the
chairs set up on the gymnasium floor to the microphone set out
for the event, where the Pronouncer (who happened to be my
mother, taking a break from her crusades against unprotected
sex) dealt them their words. The winner of each of the morning's
two bees advanced to the county spelling bee, where awaited not
only the winners of every other school's elementary bees, but also
the winners of the county's middle school bees.

After a misstep in second grade ("lavender," which I
thought ought to end like "calendar") I won the bee for Grades
1-3 in third grade. A few weeks later, on a spring Saturday, my
parents and my brothers and I piled into the station wagon and we
set out for McLouth, site of the county bee.

Normally, a spelling bee's first round is a warm-up—the
easiest words on the list, tossed to the spellers like mental chum.
But, after the rules were explained and the unfamiliar pronouncer-
lady cleared her throat to confirm that everyone inside the lunch
room could hear her, it became obvious that the 1987 Jefferson
County Spelling Bee was not going to be normal. The Pronouncer
mowed down three of the first five spellers onstage with me.

Then it was time. I was up.

I stood from the friendly confines of the bank of chairs
facing the crowd and approached the microphone, the audience
swirling in front of me. When I was settled at the front of the
stage, I made eye contact with the Pronouncer, who looked down
at her sheet, up at me, and said,

"Myopia."

I'd never heard the word before. I'd definitely never seen it. I ran the Pronouncer through all the stalling tactics I'd learned: definition, use it in a sentence, an alternate pronunciation, perhaps?

During my practice sessions, Dad insisted I say the word before and after I spelled it. It felt old-fashioned, like when he instructed my brothers and me to use two hands when we caught fly balls. We wanted to ape the Major Leaguers we saw nonchalantly putting their gloves to sky; I wanted to seem like I cared less about spelling. But the thing was, my dad was right about the fly balls. One of my dipshit PeeWee baseball teammates would invariably drop a ball he shouldn't have, trying to showboat with one hand.

"Myopia,

M-I-O-P-I-A,

Myopia."

"I'm sorry, that's incorrect," the Pronouncer-lady said, her voice clipped and ready for the next speller. I wasn't exactly surprised. But still, my parents were here, my brothers were here, even Mrs. Maloney, my beloved third-grade teacher, had made the drive.

And it had all been so abrupt.

One minute, I was standing there in front of the crowd in the long-sleeve plaid shirt and size 16 (Slim) Lee jeans my mother had selected for the occasion. The next, I was in the deep end of the pool, my hands scrabbling at the slick concrete edge, my lungs having forgotten how to work.

So, yeah, when I got to the chairs where my family was sitting, I started crying.

The next year, I was determined to atone for my mistake. (Among other things, I'd figured out that, other than "mice" and "mitochondria," almost no long-I words begin with M-I.)

I studied harder, practicing like at least one of my parents was from Pakistan. One night, when I was hung up on *why* the word "psychology" started like it did, my father said,

"Just remember: psychology, psychiatry, they start with P-S-Y. Memorize that combo."

I still think of his advice when I type either word.

Thanks to all that practice, I breezed through the fourth-and-fifth grade bee and was set for my second straight appearance in the Jefferson County Spelling Bee, this year in the sleepy town of Winchester.

There was a problem, though: the county spelling bee was scheduled the same morning as the Lake Perry Optimist's weekly basketball clinic.

Every Saturday morning that winter, my friends and I had been putting on shorts under sweatpants and reporting to the high school, where the Lake Perry Optimist Club, in conjunction with the Jefferson West High School basketball team, hosted a two-hour clinic inside the high school. There, we stretched and did ball-handling drills and half-court scrimmages. Which was lovely for our progress as little humans and basketball players, but it wasn't what got me excited about the Optimist Club's clinic. I was most pleased that the high school basketball players were there.

As a kid, I liked nothing as much as I did a high school basketball game. The gym lights seemed so bright, the band so loud, the players so grown-up, so confident, so, well, maybe not good, exactly, but at least capable of shooting underhand lay-ups—something that was thus far well beyond my basketball purview. And here they were, on Saturday mornings, paying attention to *me*.

At the end of the session that was one week before the county spelling bee, I walked up to the basketball clinic's coordinator and, thinking he was put on Earth solely to worry about the Lake Perry Optimist Club's Saturday-morning basketball clinic, asked if it would be alright if I came late to next week's because I had to go to the spelling bee first.

Of course, he said. That'll be fine.

I smiled and told him thanks as my imagination whirled into service. First, I would win the county spelling bee in Winchester. Then, I would return to Meriden to continue my basketball education under the watchful eyes of the best basketball players in the world. I would be some kind of proto-

Tony Stewart, the first driver to finish both the Indianapolis 500 and a NASCAR race on the same day.

On the morning of my attempt at an academic and athletic double-dip, I packed my basketball gear in a small duffel bag and got into the car with my mother. No family affair. No beloved third-grade teachers. We were keeping it small, traveling light, keeping it TIGHT.

At the high school in Winchester, we followed signs that led us to the auditorium, where spotlights shone down on the microphone that, I was sure, would be the conduit to my first county spelling bee win. I said goodbye to my mother and found my way to the stage, feeling like an old hand. I draped my placard over my neck, and sat down with twenty other spellers.

My first word was "corporation," which signified that someone new was in charge of the County Spelling Bee this year—someone who understood that, yeah, these kids have been studying their *tuchuses* off, but they might need a little warm-up.

I stepped to the microphone. No need for definitions, alternate pronunciations, or sentences this year. No, we just needed to DO THIS.

I rattled the letters off in a string, neglecting my father's archaic (stupid!) methodology.

"C-O-P-O-R-A-T-I-O-N"

If I'd been capable of a cocky slouch, I would have deployed it. I'd been studying for weeks! I knew words like surreptitious, facile, onomatopoeia! *Corporation*? How dare they insult my intelligence with something so elementary, so simple, so facil-

"I'm sorry, that's incorrect."

I replayed the previous eight seconds in my brain.

My god, she was right. I'd left out the first R.

This time, I didn't even make it to my mother before I started crying.

Ten minutes later, I was in the station wagon, my mother trying to console me by reminding me that I still had the basketball clinic to look forward to.

When we arrived in Meriden, I changed into my shorts and high-tops and walked into the high school, my posture weighed down by the apathetic attitude of someone who'd just had his heart broken. By the time I got into the gym, the clinic was very close to over; I got in on a few drills before the man in charge told us to find a basket and shoot free throws. I strolled to the fan-shaped basket in the southeast corner. And there, waiting underneath, was one of my heroes: Rance Bigham, the high school team's star, in his low-top black sneakers and even lower black socks. Under normal circumstances, I would have been starstruck, incapable of talking to this MAN I watched play on Friday nights in this very gym.

But today was different. Today, I didn't give a...fudge.

I told Rance that he'd "played good" the night before. Which may or may not have been true. Probably not, come to think of it. Rance Bigham thought he could shoot, and sometimes he *could* shoot. But mostly, he valued quantity of jumpshots over quality of jumpshots. And the team won just about as often as his three-pointers went in. (Approximately 20% of the time.) But still. The black shoes, the low-cut socks, the nonchalant way he carried himself? He was a New Kid on the Block; I was any one of my female classmates.

"Thanks, Paul," he said.

Wait just a gol-darn second. Rance Bigham knew my name?

I blinked. And that was sufficient as a response. There was no need to risk sullying this encounter with more words. I took my turn at the line and shot my first free throw, forgetting the spelling bee entirely. Stupid spelling bee. Who cares about spelling bees? Rance Bigham knows my name!

Then, as I was setting up for my second free throw, newly steeped in self-satisfaction thanks to my status as Someone High School Basketball Players Knew, a shadow passed over my left shoulder.

I turned. And then groaned.

Coming my way was Justin Bridges, he of my future psychological (P-S-Y!) torture during Sex Ed.; he of his own future body odor. We were only in fourth grade, but I was already terrified of him. His version of torment hadn't yet gone beyond the occasional menacing look or kick at my book bag, but I always had the sense that under the surface bubbled something more sinister. I wasn't surprised, then, when Justin walked past and knocked away the ball that was in my hands.

In college psychology, I learned about a phenomenon called "transference," which happens when one takes the emotional reaction to one event and applies it to another event. I didn't miss that question on the test, largely because of what happened when Justin knocked my basketball away, which was that I cocked my right fist and threw the first punch of my 10-year-old life.

And, oh, what a punch it was...when I conceived it. Under the harsh spotlight of reality, it was a disaster. Instead of connecting with Justin's nose like I'd wanted, it glanced off his shoulder, a flat stone on a smooth lake.

My punch's relative inefficacy didn't stop Justin's eyes from going wide, the fury that would one day make him a passable high school linebacker massing for a front-line assault. My eyes probably went wide, too, but only because of the flight part of that age-old instinctive dilemma.

Before Justin could dismember me, I was surrounded by the high school basketball players, by Rance Bigham, by the other kids around the free throw lane, everyone suddenly a peacemaker.

Someone carried Justin away, and I pretended that I needed to be carried away. In the aftermath, the coordinator tossed Justin and me from the clinic. And banned us from future sessions. My father appealed to the man's reason the following weekend: I mean, after all, they're kids, sir. But to no avail. Me and the Lake Perry Optimist's Free Basketball Clinic were no longer a match.

My "punch" made me a legend amongst the high school basketball players. One of them said, "Hey Rocky, what's up?" when he saw me before warm-ups one subsequent Friday night. My coolperson status was fleeting, though. It wasn't long before the high school basketball players forgot about my dalliance with delinquency, and I was returned to my natural state: the same fourth-grader I'd always been—the one who was far more comfortable spelling words than throwing punches; the one who would always keep a wary eye peeled when Justin Bridges was around.

The next year, as a fifth-grader, I went back to the county spelling bee. Then again as a seventh-grader. But I made no real progress at those county bees; I didn't even crack the top three. I wasn't the only kid spending his evenings with a twenty-page word list. Eighth grade was my last chance because eighth grade was the last year that kids were eligible for spelling bees. Just in time, as it happened; the spelling bee was getting decidedly less cool every year. My classmates were no longer amused by my tales from the county bee, where "some kid from Perry-Lecompton just wouldn't miss, guys!"

Spelling's fall from grace did give me one advantage: the school spelling bee was a veritable picnic now that my main rivals were occupied with pastimes like "talking to girls."

At the county bee, in my own school's gym, I survived round after round, in a sort of fugue state. When I looked up, everyone was gone—everyone, that is, but a bespectacled girl from Valley Falls.

In spelling bees, the rules change when the field is winnowed to the final two. If either lad (or lass) misses a word, the other competitor must first spell that word correctly before next spelling correctly a *new* word in order to procure the fine present.

It was like the rules to H-O-R-S-E my brothers and I used: on your last letter, you could make the previous shooter "prove" his shot by making it again.

We parried back and forth, the girl from Valley Falls and me, neither of us giving away a letter. And then, in the way that happens when getting a first period or falling in love (meaning, with far less fanfare and warning than you would have thought), she fell apart on "crustacean," adding an O for no reason that I could divine. I walked to the microphone and, with my heart in my throat, rattled off the correct spelling.

I stood there, awaiting my fate.

Don't make it a long one, I thought. I could picture almost any word, as long as it stayed under ten letters.

"Eczema," the Pronouncer-lady said. (Why these pronouncers were always women, I did not know.)

I clenched my fist near my hip in the tiniest show of celebration. I knew "eczema" back to front, front to back, middle to middle. But I'd learned enough lessons. I asked the woman to repeat herself. I asked for a definition. I told her to use it in a sentence. I said the word. I spelled the word. I said the word again. And then, I'd done what I'd set out to do way back in third grade: I'd won the Jefferson County Spelling Bee.

(And a $50 savings bond—a fine present, indeed.)

But that was not the end. Because now, a berth in the Big Time awaited me: I was going to the Kansas State Spelling Bee.

On the Saturday morning of the state bee, I put on a mustard yellow long-sleeve shirt and a pair of black slacks and, after a hearty breakfast of scrambled eggs and too-dry toast, I got into the white Plymouth Grand Voyager my parents had purchased after the arrival of my youngest brother and we drove to Washburn University in Topeka, where I got in a check-in line with the other 104 county champions. (Kansas has a lot of counties. The fifth-most in the country, as it inexplicably turns out.)

Since the county bee, I'd ramped my practice sessions to an almost absurd degree; I was spelling after school, after dinner, on weekends. I thought about how words were spelled in my sleep, while I was eating, while I should have been coming up with cute things to say to Lisa Zerr in Language Arts.

Sure, I was just a kid from a tiny town in Kansas, but so what?

There wasn't any real reason I shouldn't win, was there?

I mean, why not me?

These were the things I was telling myself in the check-in line. It was a time before cellular phones, before iPods; I was alone with my thoughts.

Until I felt a tap on my shoulder.

I turned to find a tall girl in a flowery blue dress looking at me. "Where's your county?"

I couldn't imagine why this was important.

"Uh," I said, my brow wrinkling up like it did when I was confused. "It's Jefferson County. Just north of here."

She nodded. Then, after the sort of pause you encounter when you talk to a psychopath who doesn't understand social cues, I said, "What about you?"

"Gove," she said. "Way out west." She smiled and leaned toward me. "By the way, I came over here because I saw you when you walked in. I told the other girls you were mine."

I couldn't have turned redder if she'd told me I'd forgotten to put on pants. What was happening? I was worth *claiming*? I mean, this girl was even *cute!*

Of course, just because girls were suddenly coming up to me and saying hello in the check-in line didn't mean I had suddenly sprouted skills in flirtation. After the Girl From Gove County said the nice thing she said, it was my turn to check in. When I was finished, she was at the check-in station next to me, busy getting a placard of her own. Should I wait? Should I not?

No! I decided. *I'm here to spell words, dammit!*

The state bee started like a spelling bee should—no first-round destruction like had happened in McLouth in 3rd grade. Then, though, the words' difficulty skyrocketed like someone in charge had left the stove on at home and the stage began to empty out. But I danced through the second round, the third round, the fourth round. When I looked up again, there were 40 of us left, my Spelling Bee Girlfriend included. I spelled another word; there were 32 of us. Then Gove County missed and waved at me as she left the stage. Another word, another count. 20 kids. Then another word, then another count. 11. Then another word and, what in the holy heck? There were only seven of us left. Six kids between me and a win. Six kids between me and a trip to Washington D.C. and a spot in the national spelling bee.

I forced a deep breath as we reshuffled, moving to the front row of the stage, where the lights were brighter and the walk to the microphone was shorter. The first of our number went to the microphone. Then he was done, victim of overthinking a –tion suffix that he turned into a –cion suffix.

Five.

And I was next.

I told myself that all I had to do was get one right and I would get to sit down again.

I stepped to the microphone, the Ban deodorant I used because that's what my parents used fighting valiantly against my 13-year-old armpits.

My word came from below me, like it had all morning—a

disembodied voice out of the darkness beneath the stage. The woman had probably been practicing her diction all week, for moments like these.

"Metallurgical."

Metallurgical, I thought. *I've seen this word. But damn, it's long.*

I took a deep breath, telling myself to slow down. There was no need to repeat a Winchester; no need to rush.

"Can you define it?"

"Metallurgical: of or related to the study of minerals and their properties."

That made sense. Metals, basically. I could do this.

"Can you use it in a sentence?"

"Barry studied the metallurgical properties of steel beams at the Colorado School of Mines."

I licked my lips and leaned toward the microphone.

And then, something snapped and I started thinking.

The National Spelling Bee? I'm not that good at spelling.

All morning, I'd been cool, calm, and that other C-word that, in my panicked condition, I probably couldn't spell. I'd even chatted with a girl!

But now? Now, none of this made sense. If my parents had been close enough to see the look in my eyes, they would have noticed that something had gone very wrong.

I was shaken, scared, everything I hadn't been. But there wasn't much to be done. I couldn't call time. I had a word to spell. So I took one more deep breath and launched in.

"M-E-T-A-L-U-R-G-I-C-A-L"

"I'm sorry, that's incorrect."

My mouth open, I took a step back toward the chairs. I'd gotten so used to walking back and forth between the chairs and the microphone that I hadn't considered where I was supposed to go when I missed. Then I saw her: another woman, probably the owner of several tote bags from the local public television station, motioning my way, off to my left. I walked off the stage in a daze, searching for my parents in the theater's darkness. When I found them, my mother gave me a hug; Dad gave me one of his patented shrug/smiles. This time, I didn't cry. I was too shocked.

After a month, the scorched feeling brought on by my loss began to fade. It was time to think about the end of the school year, about summer baseball, about Boy Scout Camp, about high school the next fall. I didn't know what happened to the kid who won the state spelling bee my year—whether, when he went to Washington, he finished first or last or somewhere in between. I did know that I probably wouldn't have had much of a chance at the national bee. Those kids were maniacs.

That didn't stop me from wondering what might have been, had I stayed the course—if I'd been able to stay in the cognitive sweet spot I'd found while outlasting the 100 spellers who fell before me.

Some of my second-guessing was mitigated by the awareness that my spelling days were over. For six years, I'd been a competitive speller (if you could call it that). But then middle school ended, and my spelling career went with it. Simple as that. And that was probably for the best, wasn't it? My spelling ability didn't *matter*. It didn't *matter* if I could spell metallurgical, or myopia, or corporation.

Did it?

Well, actually, yes.

A harsh truth about our finite lives is that nothing we do *matters*. Barring vampire bites or extreme advances in medical technology, we'll be around for but a stutter of time's long spelling bee.

So we find things to care about while we still can.

For me, one of those things caused me to spend childhood evenings in my bedroom running through lists of words with my father. It taught me a lesson about confidence. It made me ignore cute girls who came up to talk to me. And it inspired me to cock my fist and throw the first and—unless things have changed drastically—only punch of my life.

All on behalf of something that is, by all reasonable measures, pretty much worthless: the ability to correctly spell words in English.

All so my life had meaning. To me.

The girl from the band squeezes my hand. When I look over at her, I see the scrubland of Eastern Colorado flashing past her window.

"Thanks," she says, her eyes meeting mine. Her voice is calmer now.

I can tell that I have accomplished what I set out to do—what most stories set out to do—which is to make her feel a little less alone.

I can also tell that I haven't solved her problems completely. But stories can't always solve problems completely.

"What's wrong?"

She turns to the window.

"What's wrong is that you're right. You liked spelling—or basketball—enough that you tried to punch a kid."

She looks at me and shakes her head.

"Dork."

"Hey," I say. "Did you forget about the part where the girl rolled up on me before the state spelling bee?"

"Exactly! And even her you shut down because it was enough, the spelling. That's how the band used to be. But then it got all mixed up in the crowds, and the videos, and the magazines, and, you know."

"Yes, I do," I say.

My voice is quiet when I say this, because she's right. I did the same thing with basketball. I changed it from something I cared about because it made me happy to something I cared about because it made other people happy.

My voice is also quiet because I know she's got an existential crisis coming like a patch of ice in the road.

And the best I can do is hold onto her hand and keep driving.

LOS ANGELES

A Saturday night

"So, the referee bounces me the ball, like referees always do. And I take a deep breath, like *I* always do. Of course, this is a pretty terrible coping mechanism for the chills that are running up and down my back and have left me weak in the knees, but not like SWV."

This gets a grin out of her, which is a little surprising; I wasn't sure she was old enough to know SWV.

"And?" she says, swirling the purple wine in her glass.

"And, desperate for something familiar, I pick out one of the hooks that holds the net to the rim—because those are the same in every gym."

"Clever," she says.

She's getting it.

I thought she might; she seems smarter than most of the people I might have met on a night like this. And she's from Missouri—she was in an issue called *Girls of the Big XII*—so she might understand the significance of Midwestern basketball rivalries.

"I tell myself I have eyes only for this spot because I'm trying to push from my mind one important fact: if I make this free throw, I will clinch a win inside Allen Fieldhouse, home to the Kansas Jayhawks. Which almost no one does, as I know all too well, having grown up a massive fan of those Kansas Jayhawks."

"Stupid Kansas fans."

Missouri people and Kansas people have a good-natured rivalry that wasn't always so good-natured: John Brown and Quantrill's Raiders and all that.

"Exactly," I say. "I dribble twice, like I've done since middle school basketball camp, when they told us to shoot our free throws the same way each time. The crowd behind the clear backboard waits, ready to sway from right to left just as I shoot, like I used to see it do on my parents' TV. The crowd does its part, tick-tocking across. I let go of the ball. The ball hits the front of the rim. The ball hits the back of the rim."

I look at her, wanting her to ask what happens next because, now that I've started, I want to tell her this story. This surprises me because, for a while, this didn't seem possible. But maybe it's been long enough since I quit playing that I'm ready to tell basketball stories again. Or maybe it's because she caught me unawares; I didn't think I'd meet anyone I'd want to tell any stories when I arrived at the gates to the Playboy Mansion, brought there by a famous basketball player Scott knows, because of course Scott knows him and of course I'm roaming Los Angeles with Scott again, now that I've moved back here to get my writing career off the tarmac.

But then she and a friend walked up and started talking to me at 1:30 in the morning.

They were both Playmates. *Are* Playmates, I should say; they corrected me immediately. Once a Playmate, always a Playmate. Like a President.

The one from Missouri—the one I'm hoping will ask me what happens next—gave me a tour of the Mansion grounds. Then she said we should go back to her place for a glass of wine. And that was not an invitation a single person like me was going to turn down. The girl from the band and me: we made it all of a month in Los Angeles.

The band did not survive the move, either.

"OK, so, did your free throw go in or not?"

I wink at her.

"Well, that I can't tell you yet, because this isn't *just* a basketball story. Which means we need to go back a ways, so you know why."

She wiggles her wine glass.

"Am I going to need more of this?"

I nod. And away we go.

12

Iowa State vs Kansas, 9 pm ET/8 pm CT

I joined my first basketball team in sixth grade. After twenty seconds on the court, my coach walked onto the court to call an exasperated timeout before striding to the spot on the floor where I was futilely trying to figure out how to "guard" my opponent. He moved me bodily to the other side of the boy.

No, Paul, *between* him and the basket.

After that, I picked things up pretty quickly, and it wasn't long before I was in love.

In eighth grade, my gym teacher, who would one day preside over the end of my *base*ball career when I stopped a curve ball with my face, asked me each day how much I'd practiced the night before. An hour, I'd say with pride. Sometimes an hour and a half. Sometimes two hours. It didn't matter to me; there was nothing I liked more than being on the gravel driveway in back of my parents' house: just the ball, the basket, and me. I felt like a weirdo everywhere else. But there in the driveway, with my only judge the swish of the net, I was free.

By high school, I was harboring dreams of playing basketball in college. But not just at any college. I wanted to play at the University of Kansas, once home to Wilt Chamberlain, to Dean Smith, and to James Naismith, the inventor of basketball. It didn't hurt that both my parents had graduated from there. Or that we lived thirty minutes from campus. Then there was the memory of that night in 1988, when Kansas won a national championship on the backs of several college kids whose names

I'll remember forever. It was the second-best night of my life, right after the night in 1985 when Daryl Motley caught the final out in right field and the Kansas City Royals won the World Series. (As a child, my happiness was very much tied to the performances of my favorite sports teams.)

My aspirations of one day playing for KU hardly made me unique; everyone in Northeast Kansas who'd ever put his hands on a basketball had some specious claim to why he would someday be a Jayhawk. There was one difference: as a junior in high school, I'd grown to 6'7", could handle myself around the basket, *and* could make a three-point shot. So, my dreams seemed at least reasonable. For me, playing at KU wouldn't be winning a multimillion-dollar Powerball Jackpot; it'd be more like hitting the $10,000 grand prize on one of those scratch-off tickets that steal money from poor people.

I spent the summer after that junior year playing more basketball than any human who wasn't in the NBA. Tournaments on weekends, summer league games on weeknights, "exposure" camps during the week. I'd found an AAU basketball team—the oh-so-hokily named Kansas Pride—that was happy to have me join a frontline of similar-sized white guys from other small towns in the area. We were good, but not quite as good as Kansas City's AAU juggernaut, the Children's Mercy Hospital (CMH) 76ers, home to future NBA washouts Korleone Young and JaRon Rush and future Duke star Corey Maggette, who eventually played 14 seasons in the NBA.

(In our defense, we weren't getting paid to play. CMH "coach" Myron Piggie would later be convicted on conspiracy charges for paying $35,000 to high school players on the CMH roster. Which helped explain why the CMH players always had matching shoes. And such good players.)

I hadn't been named to any of the fancy Top 100 recruiting lists populated by Young, Rush, and Maggette. I wasn't as speedy as I would get when my body's hormonal dosage kicked up from the trickle it was set on and my jerseys still hung off me like I was a scarecrow. But that summer, I blossomed into something more than the dominant small town player I was assumed to be, and on July 1 the recruiting calls started. The only problem: the voices on the other end weren't the ones I wanted to hear. My most ardent suitors were employed by the likes of North Dakota State University, the University of Missouri at Rolla, Colorado School of Mines, and Northern State University which, confusingly, is in South Dakota.

Not a peep from Kansas. Hell, I didn't even hear from Kansas State. And Kansas State was terrible.

This was not how this was supposed to go.

One of the disembodied voices coming out of the top end of the cordless phone that hung in my parents' kitchen belonged to Steve Krafcisin, an assistant coach at the University of North Dakota. He'd played at North Carolina AND Iowa and was, as he told me, the only player to score in NCAA Final Fours with two different teams.

Most of the coaches who talked to me did so as if they were reading off cue cards like the ones I'd prepared for my first date with Kelly Stepka. But not Coach K, as, predictably, he asked to be called. We had real conversations about real topics: sports, weather, girls, his wife, how he'd ended up in North Dakota. And, in another departure from the norm, he had a sense of humor; he sent me recruiting letters featuring cut-out pictures of supermodels with dialog bubbles that read, "I hope Paul comes to North Dakota!"

This was more like what I'd thought recruitment would be like. All I needed now was for Steve Krafcisin's voice to be replaced by that of Matt Doherty, the head assistant at Kansas.

By the fall, the caliber of my suitors had increased slightly, probably because of the natural reordering process that occurs in college basketball recruitment: as it became clear that the guy above me was going to go to somewhere above *them*, the better schools ratcheted down their expectations. I was hearing from smaller Division I schools, most of them on the East Coast, and most of them of that breed of college known to be associated with smart white kids like me: the Ivy Leagues. The year before, I'd done well enough on the PSAT that I'd been named a National Merit Finalist. Thusly, in the eyes of Ivy League basketball coaches, I was as attractive as a Cinnabon stand on Cheat Day.

On the basketball recruitment calendar, September is home visit month. I granted as many coaches as I could the opportunity to navigate Jefferson County's gravel roads en route to the Shirley acreage (two acres). The coaches were mostly the same, befitting coaches who were all in the places they were for about the same reason—they were honest and decent men, both of which are characteristics generally detrimental to big-time college coaching success.

Dartmouth. Holy Cross. Air Force. Harvard. Missouri-Rolla. Washburn.

And the University of North Dakota, of course.

Coach K was just as great in person as he was on the phone, laughing about how his knees almost touched his chin when he sat down in our old rocking chair.

Those coaches didn't tell me I'd someday play in the NBA. They didn't even say I'd play if I came to their schools. "You'll have the same chance as everyone," they said. Which was about all I could ask for; it's just I wanted to ask for it somewhere else.

One day that winter, while most of the coaches who were recruiting me were focusing their attention on the teams they already had, my father said he had an idea. At first, I protested, it JUST WASN'T WHAT PEOPLE DID. But after 24 hours of teenaged stubbornness, I came around. The alternative was a home at someplace like the University of Missouri-Rolla, where, because it was an engineering school, the male:female ratio was 12:1. "But don't worry!" that team's assistant coach had said. "The players get all the girls!"

I wrote down every place I could conceivably imagine playing—maybe not Duke, Kentucky, or North Carolina, but Northwestern, Western Kentucky, and North Carolina-Charlotte. And on, and on, and on. When I was done, I had a list of 60 schools. Using a directory I dug up at the Topeka Public Library, I found out the names of the head coaches at every one of them. And then I fired up WordPerfect on the Hewlett-Packard that resided in my parents' bedroom and churned out my letters, in which I explained who I was and what I believed: that, in spite of the fact that I played basketball for a high school in a town of 700 people, I was good enough to play at their respective schools.

Most of the coaches didn't respond, but a few of them did. At Oklahoma, Kelvin Sampson wrote that he appreciated the initiative I'd taken, but that he didn't have any scholarships left. Northwestern said they were full, too. And from Iowa State, in a leaning scrawl, head coach Tim Floyd said he, too, was sorry, but that he couldn't come up with a scholarship for me.

While Tim Floyd was writing to me, I was tearing up high school basketball courts all over Northeast Kansas, fueled in no small part by all those rejections. Sometimes during my senior year, I'd only score 20, but a lot of the time, I scored 30, an accomplishment made all the more difficult thanks to the zones, the double-teams, and boxes-and-ones that were engineered by opposing small-town coaches. By season's end, I'd averaged 25 points and 12 rebounds, shooting a nearly unbelievable 70% from the field while also blocking four shots every game—leading the state in both categories.

And we were winning. We had a coach who encouraged us to race up and down the court, a point guard—Jed Traxler, who'd transferred to our school before our junior year—who could throw me an alley-oop, and a three-point shooter to take the pressure off the inside. Together, we took our tiny high school to the state tournament for the first time in school history.

Surely someone would notice all that, I thought.

And so they did. The University of Missouri-Kansas City (UMKC) was interested. So was Wichita State. And Drake University in Des Moines.

Better, but still not the place I wanted. Sure, I'd written those letters to schools all over the country. But I hadn't given up hope on Kansas.

By March, most of the high school seniors who were going to play college basketball the following autumn had already signed their letters of intent, or were about to. Like a sophomore girl who's three months pregnant, I needed to make a decision. So, after we lost by seven in the first round of the state tournament, I visited Dartmouth, Harvard, the University of Vermont, and the University of North Dakota.

At Dartmouth, I saw my first real party and thought maybe Hanover was the right place for me. But then I came home, and we figured out that my parents would have to pay $15,000 a year for me to go to keggers with rich white people.

Harvard was expensive, too, of course, but it was Harvard! Or so said our family's resident Harvard grad, my uncle Tom.

In Vermont, the coach told me he thought I could be a Rhodes Scholar.

And at North Dakota, true to form, Coach K made the competition look clownishly incompetent. My hotel room was filled with green and white balloons. When I got to the gym, on the scoreboard above, a message read, "Welcome, Paul, to the home of your future dunks!"

Here, I was wanted. Here, I would succeed. Here, I would probably become the team's star. But at a Division II school. After the visit, I told Coach K how much I appreciated everything he'd done, and that I'd miss him and the models, but the thing was: one way or another, I was going to play Division I basketball.

He was disappointed, he told me, but he wasn't surprised.

"I might even be able to help," he said.

Before taking a job at the University of North Dakota, Coach K had been an assistant at Iowa State. When I told him to buzz off, he called Iowa State's head coach, Tim Floyd, and told him about this kid no one knew about, but who he thought was good enough to play in the Big XII: the sports conference that had just been formed by all the former members of the Big 8 and half the members of the Southwestern Conference.

Floyd had just given away his last scholarship. He had an idea, though. One of his former assistants was at Southern Mississippi. Why didn't he put us in touch? The next day I took a call in the high school library: it was the head coach at Southern Mississippi, offering me a scholarship. This was a little more like it.

A few days later, I heard from the head coach at Davidson College in North Carolina. He was willing to fly to Kansas to watch me work out. Soon after his visit, I went to Charlotte to walk the campus at Davidson, the smallest Division I school in the United States. And the only one that still did all of its students' laundry.

Then, when I got back from North Carolina, two pieces of news were waiting. After a little research, my mother had learned that, at Iowa State, status as a National Merit Finalist was worth a full academic scholarship. She'd gotten back in touch with the basketball office, and Tim Floyd had started paying attention again. If I wanted, I could come to Ames on that academic scholarship and play for the team. Technically, I would be a walk-on (a non-athletic scholarship player), but Floyd promised not to tell anyone.

But Iowa State would have to wait because the other piece of news was that Matt Doherty had called.

Roy Williams wanted me to come to Lawrence to talk.

The night before the big day, I conjured various dream scenarios, all of which involved roaring Allen Fieldhouse crowds. Raef LaFrentz, then the Jayhawks starting power forward, high-fiving me after a lay-up. Paul Pierce, whose first practice I'd watched as a high school junior, picking me up off the floor after I'd taken a charge. Jacque Vaughn, smiling at me as we both ran back on defense after I'd made a short jumper.

In the morning, I put on my best St. John's Bay long-sleeve, cursed the pair of whiteheads that had made an inconvenient appearance overnight, and got into the Grand Voyager with my parents for the drive to Lawrence. After we found the basketball offices, and after we waited the requisite fifteen minutes, we were ushered into Roy Williams's plush office. His desk was a monstrosity, something out of the mediocre John Grisham novels I was reading at the time. Then the man himself appeared, his voice all honey and clover just like in the press conferences I'd watched. He offered us the chairs across from his desk. My eyes wandered to the pictures of him coaching various national teams, his arms around Jim Boeheim, Dean Smith, Gene Keady. And then we sat, and in that same accent, Roy Williams crushed my boyhood dreams.

He hadn't called because he wanted me to come to Kansas. He'd called because he wanted me to go to Davidson. As it turned out, that random call from Davidson hadn't been all that random; someone at Kansas had called Davidson's coach about me. But that wasn't the worst of it. While I weighed what I was being told, Williams dropped the deathblow, telling me that I needed face up to the fact that I wasn't good enough to play in the Big XII.

Stunned, I asked about Iowa State, Kansas's Big XII rival. "They seem pretty interested," I said.

Both Williams and Doherty scoffed.

"You don't want to go to Iowa State. Just go to Davidson. It'd be a great place for you."

Were they trying to do a favor to an old friend? Were they

trying to keep me out of the Big XII in case I blossomed and came back to haunt them? Or were they just trying to get me out of their office so they could get back to smoking cigars or drinking port or playing cards or whatever it is that people do in a room with carpet that's an inch and a half tall?

I never knew, exactly. I did know that they were right about one thing: Davidson would have been a great place for me. My visit had happened on a spring weekend so gorgeous that I almost signed up on the spot. Plus, the coach at Davidson was a Paul Shirley FAN. And Davidson wasn't some Division I also-ran. The team would eventually be known for producing NBA super-duper-star Steph Curry.

After I staggered out of Roy Williams's office, and after my mother vowed that she'd never again cheer for Kansas, and after I said no to Wichita State, and Drake, and UMKC, whose head coach had come to my high school with a letter of intent that he wanted me to sign on the spot, my options were set.

Davidson. Or Iowa State.

Davidson seemed like the safe option, even though it was farther away. I'd be welcomed there, hailed—maybe not as the future conquering hero, but at least with open arms. Iowa State was a risk. Sure, Tim Floyd had said no one would ever know I was technically a walk-on. But could I trust him? Would I really have a chance to play?

One late spring evening, with my brothers treating me like the rubber tires in a bumper-car track, I sat down at the kitchen table and made a column of Pros and Cons. Iowa State was closer; Davidson was friendlier. Iowa State had an engineering program; Davidson was a better school. I'd spoken to Tim Floyd once; I talked to the Davidson coach nearly every day.

My list—organized, reasonable, and fittingly obsessive-compulsive—solved nothing. What did help make up my mind was the searing pain of unequivocal rejection. Until Roy Williams told me from behind his massive desk that I wasn't good enough to play in the Big XII, the rejections had been passive—an unreturned letter, a phone call that never happened. My desire for retribution had been similarly ephemeral. I wanted to prove these people wrong, but my anger didn't have a focal point. Now, though, I had something to hold onto.

After I called Davidson, the coach wrote me a four-page letter in which he told me how much he'd enjoyed getting to know me. It made me wonder about my decision to go to Iowa State. As did the first day of pick-up basketball in Ames the following autumn, when future NBA first-round draft pick Kelvin Cato spun out and threw down a vicious slam dunk on top of my head. As did the first weekend of official practice, when we had a pair of grueling three-hour sessions on Saturday and another pair on Sunday. As did the first slate of games, during which I was mired at the end of the bench. As did laundry day, and every time I was out of clean socks.

Every so often, though, little tendrils of life shot up. Practices when I'd outsmart Cato with a timely pump fake. An early game at the University of Iowa, before which Coach Floyd took me aside to tell me I was going to play, a lot, and into which I was inserted because one of my senior teammates was ineligible.

I scored a quick eight points. More important, though, was the feeling I got on the court. I wasn't good enough yet, but the path was getting clearer.

Roy Williams was going to be wrong about me.

We made it all the way to the NCAA tournament's Sweet Sixteen my freshman year, finishing with a 22-9 record thanks to five beloved seniors—five beloved seniors our fans would miss the following season, my sophomore year, when our 12-18 record helped drive Tim Floyd into the arms of the Chicago Bulls.

This was a problem.

Coach Floyd hadn't been all blessings and buttercups, but I could tell he liked me—that he had plans for me. One day during Christmas break my sophomore year, he'd asked me to come with him to Des Moines after practice. He had to speak at a fundraiser, he said.

When we got there, he told me I was going onstage.

"But there are, like, 700 people out there," I said.

"You'll be fine," he said with the same wry grin that charmed most everyone he came in contact with.

And I was.

Here was a man who had confidence in me—who'd said far nicer things to me than my own father—and now he was leaving, in the heart of my college career, and there was no way of knowing who the athletic director would pick to replace him. But, I reckoned, there wasn't much I could do about any of that. So, that summer, I went back to my parents' house with myriad athletic clichés on the brain.

I was:

A) not going to let anything stop me!
B) ready to take on the world!
C) going to lift harder, run faster, and work longer than anyone else!

I was ridiculous; it was like I was writing slogans for those No Fear shirts I'd once favored.

But I was also serious. I knew I was close to realizing the dreams I'd carried around since my summer at Skinner's Nursery, and I was going to do everything I could to:

D) make my dreams come true!

During the day, I trained at my old high school, lifting weights in the fetid dungeon where I'd once watched Darin Densmore fracture a vertebra doing a clean-and-jerk. At night, I drove to Kansas City for summer league games in a brick-oven gym near the Paseo, which is a street where people are sometimes shot.

By the middle of the summer, the clichés were lining up; I was getting bigger, stronger, better. I noticed that I was far less afraid of my opponents now; I was starting to figure out how my body worked, and my teammates on that summer league team were taking note, often throwing me the ball and telling me to "go to work!" and "take it to him!"

(It is difficult to be etymologically creative when you are out of breath.)

Then came the news: Iowa State had hired a man named Larry Eustachy, who'd most recently been the head coach at Utah State.

My initial research turned up some alarming data. Most of Eustachy's players at Utah State only stayed for a year, or maybe two, which did nothing to counter what I was hearing about his tyrannical attitude toward coaching.

Then the rumors got less rumor-y.

At the same time that I was thinking about my third year of college, my brother Dan was thinking about his first. He was headed off to play basketball at a college in Kansas called Pittsburg State, and as luck would have it, one of his new teammates had just transferred in from Utah State.

I called Dan's new teammate to ask what Eustachy was like.

Toward the end of what had already been an alarming conversation, he said, "Look, you seem like a decent enough guy. I'm going to tell you in no uncertain terms: you do not want to play for that man."

Shaken, I called the man himself. When I did, his wife answered.

"This is Stacy."

I said, "Your name is Stacy Eu*stachy*?"

Great start, Paul.

When my new coach got on the phone, I asked him my questions.

Did he know about me?

Had Coach Floyd said anything?

Was the starting job I'd earned still mine?

All I wanted was a little reassurance—for him to tell me to calm down, that he'd loved the way I'd played in some game or another.

But reassurance was not forthcoming.

"You'll have the same chance as everyone else," he said.

This was no longer what I wanted to hear.

From the outside, the participants in college basketball and football seem to have hit the jackpot. The colors, the pageantry, the fans: these things make college sports look like a wonderland. I had once thought this, too. If someone had told me in high school that I would someday get to play major college basketball, I would have asked what deal I'd have to make with the devil.

However, when you're inside the machine, it's a different story. You're tired. You're overworked. Grown men are screaming at you, and you realize how much money is being made and how little of it you're seeing. Sure, the fans like you, but their patience is short. There were players before you. There will be players after you.

Oh, and you are 20 years old with no one to guide you or to advocate on your behalf.

What if I went back to Iowa State and Larry Eustachy didn't like how I played?

What if he was already trying to find my replacement?

What if he was already holding a grudge because I'd noticed his wife's rhyme-y name?

With the whys and the what ifs roiling in my brain, an idea popped up—an imperfect solution to an imperfect problem.

I called my high school coach and I told him to get in touch with Kansas. Roy Williams would surely be excited about having me come play for him now that I'd proved my worth as a Big XII basketball player.

My coach told me he'd see what he could find out. And I went back to training and playing those games near the Paseo in Kansas City, getting ready for a season whose location I didn't yet know.

But whatever; I was big and strong and 20 and invincible!

Near the end of one of our games, I went up for a rebound. It was a lot like any other rebound, except that when I came down I slipped on the gym's sweaty floor. I lost my balance and smashed my right elbow, opening it all the way to a ligament, which shone bright white in its little tissue taco. And that was alarming, I thought. My dad agreed, and we went for stitches at the hospital in Topeka where my mother had once worked. The doctor on call said I should probably have some antibiotics, too. I was on a low-level course for the acne that was still plaguing me in college. I asked if that was sufficient.

Sure, he said.

Three days later, my arm had swollen and was oddly hot, so I went to the offices of our favorite orthopedist, where a doctor pronounced that the swelling was a result only of the trauma of the injury. He put me in a half-cast and sent me home.

That night, I was sitting in our ancient rocking chair, idly watching television. My mother came over to check on me.

"Do you feel OK?" she asked.

I shrugged and she put her hand on my forehead.

I had, as Bad Company would have sung it, a fever of a hundred and three.

We rushed to the emergency room at the same hospital, where a new doctor recut wound *sans stupéfiant,* which is a common French phrase I just made up to mean they couldn't use any lidocaine to numb the site as it would contaminate the sample they needed to send to the lab.

By the time I was done hyperventilating from the combination of the fever and the pain that results when someone cuts into your naked flesh with a scalpel, we had the verdict: a fair number of *staphylococcus* bacteria had invaded the bursa in my elbow.

I had what is commonly known as a staph infection.

I was not, in fact, invincible.

Doctors get panicky about bacterial infections—a fact with which I would become well-acquainted once my brother Dan grew up and became an infectious disease doctor. Nurses also get pretty panicky about them—a fact with which I would become well-acquainted right then.

My mother was never routinely sympathetic toward her sons when they were sick. This is because, before her stint with the county health department, she'd worked as a nurse, first at the Veteran's Administration hospital near where I was born and then at the regular hospital where I was now about to be admitted and put on IV antibiotics.

"Oh, you've got a cold? At least you don't have leukemia."

"Oh, there's a splinter in your hand? At least you have a hand."

Nursing has a way of putting things in perspective.

However, there is one benefit to having a nurse for a mother: when something serious comes up, like a staph infection raging inside the elbow of her eldest son, she goes into *action.*

She was on the doctors like a drill sergeant, but not in the way that most mortals might have been, which would be to wonder why someone had accepted that whatever antibiotics I was on were sufficient, or to ask why no one had caught the staph infection earlier that day.

She was only interested in solving the problem in front of her: getting me upstairs and making sure I didn't lose an arm.

Meanwhile, I wasn't doing much thinking at all—extreme fevers having that effect on people. I was mostly worried about when I would be able to close my eyes, because the fever and all the painkillers they'd pumped into me after the scalpel work—these things had me *sleepy*.

So it was with only partial interest in the situation that I watched my parents close the door to my hospital room, telling me they'd be back in the morning.

It is usually lazy and possibly disingenuous to skip to the next part of a story by saying, "And the next thing I knew..."

However, in this case, it was the truth that the next thing I knew, my parents were walking through the door.

And then they weren't walking. Or one of them wasn't, anyway.

My mom was rushing to my bedside, her eyes wide and her nostrils flared. She grabbed my arm.

"Paul! Have they not started your antibiotics?"

"Uh..."

Like I said, I wasn't using a shortcut when I said, "The next thing I knew."

My mom's eyes went wide and she whirled for the door.

I can only imagine what happened at the nurses' station in terms of the supernatural. Like, my mom sprouting scaly wings and turning into a demon.

And rightfully so. Someone had forgotten to start the IV antibiotics that had been deemed urgent the night I was admitted to the hospital where, in addition to having once worked, she'd given birth to all three of my brothers.

I'll never know, of course, whether I was close to losing my arm, or to any of the other catastrophes that might have befallen my body if the staph infection had gone unchecked. I also do not know how much of the bill for my three-day stay in the hospital my parents had to pay, but my educated guess is None Of It.

I do know that when I got out of the hospital, it was with a port in my arm through which IV antibiotics were delivered for the next two weeks during daily trips back to the hospital.

Thanks to all this trauma and the fact that I couldn't work out while my body recovered from its invasion, I also lost twenty pounds I didn't have to lose.

All of this while all manner of machinations had probably been going on at Iowa State.

And at Kansas.

Sometime during my recovery, a chill flushed my spine: I'd told my high school coach to call Kansas, hadn't I?

Regret poured through me in a way that is familiar to anyone who's checked the messages they sent after a night made hazy by drinking. My call had made a lot of sense when I'd been a hale athletic specimen that almost any college program would be happy to have. It made a whole lot less sense now that I'd returned to looking like a scarecrow.

The real problem was this one: by asking my coach to call Kansas, I'd already largely committed to carrying through with *going* to Kansas. If the new coach at Iowa State—this Eustachy fellow—found out I was considering leaving, well, that's probably why someone first applied the phrase "burning bridges" to situations that didn't involve actual bridges.

I dialed my high school coach with even more fear than when I'd called Kelly Stepka for the first time.

"Coach?"

"Yeah?"

"Uh, did you call Kansas?"

There was a pause.

"No, Paul, I didn't. It felt a little disloyal."

I don't know that my sigh of relief was audible. I do know that it was a conflicted sigh of relief. Because, on the one hand, my high school coach had inadvertently saved me from a storm of confusion. And he wasn't *wrong*; I had to be thankful for what I'd gotten so far from Iowa State.

But on the other, he'd sorta, kinda taken my destiny into his own hands. And what I'd gotten from Iowa State I mostly owed to the man who'd just left. Then there was the quote from my brother's new teammate.

You do not want to play for that man.

But I'd had enough conflict for one summer, so I reported to my now-familiar campus, telling no one I'd had designs on never being there again.

In my first encounter with my new coach, the husband of Stacy Eustachy did nothing to allay my concerns about his interpersonal skills. When I was finished telling him the story of my terrifying summer, he said, "Well, at least you weren't like the guy I was reading about a few days ago. He got a staph infection while sailing across the Atlantic by himself and had to cut off his own arm."

OK, well, you're not wrong, Coach.

But jeez.

Thanks to the staph infection and thanks to a long-term strategy Eustachy was cooking up, it was decided that I was going to spend the season as a "red shirt"—a player who can practice, but not play. The plan was for me to gain weight and strength while we awaited the arrival of a couple of recruits that were going to make us far better the following season.

Then, even that plan fell apart. When I recovered from the staph infection, a sharp pain in my pelvis led to the discovery of an avulsion fracture in my right ischium—the bone in your pelvis that makes it look like a poorly drawn heart.

My hamstring had pulled a piece of this bone away, which explained the stabbing pain anytime I leaned over to pull on a pair of socks. This was on top of the staph infection. And those on top of the fact that Eustachy had never seen me play.

I faded into the background—a ghost relegated to the sidelines during practice and street clothes during games, ignored by my coaches and teammates. They were getting distance from me, like I was a leper or an ex-girlfriend.

I couldn't blame them. I didn't know if I'd be able to play college basketball again.

There was, though, one thing I could do: lift weights. So, each day, as my teammates started practice, I reported to the weight room, where I listened to Zack de la Rocha rage while I took out my frustrations on the assorted weightlifting apparatuses available to me.

When I'd gotten to college, I weighed 200 pounds and could bench-press 185 of them. Which, by the standards of college basketball, would be labeled "terrible."

By the end of that redshirt season, I weighed 230 and could bench-press 330. Which, by the standards of Larry Eustachy, would be labeled as "acceptable." But which, by the standards of most people, would be labeled as "nearly superhuman."

As winter turned to spring I was cleared to practice. On the court, I noticed that my newfound brawn provided me with a new set of options. If I wasn't scoring points or getting rebounds, I could keep other people from doing those things. Before, I'd relied on my wits on the court. Now, I was relying on my body and in the process becoming that which I'd once resented—the physical specimen who throws himself around the court like he's the disc in a game of air hockey.

But, I told myself, it would be worth it. Because a thing that is usually true about guys who are big and play hard: a basketball coach will find a way to get those guys on the court, even if that coach is the sort of asshole who, when you explain your staph infection to him, shrugs and tells you that at least you didn't have to cut off your arm.

We started the following season—my junior year—on a sour note, losing two of our first three games. But we found the melody after that, winning 22 of the next 23 and rising to #14 in the national polls while also jostling for position atop the Big XII conference. Despite his prickly demeanor (or perhaps because of it), Eustachy had done a masterful job of pairing incumbent superstar Marcus Fizer with Iowa State's newest toy, Brooklyn playground legend Jamaal Tinsley.

Next up was a game in the home of the team with which we were jostling at the top of the conference table: the University of Kansas. The game was on ESPN, part of that network's "Big Monday" coverage.

It had been a year and a half since the staph infection and the memory of my dalliance with Kansas had been replaced by a familiar narrative: the one that featured Roy Williams telling me I would never be good enough to play in the Big XII.

And yet, here I was, *Roy*, doing exactly that.

The week before the game, I stayed for an extra hour after each practice, shooting free throws as the image of Roy Williams' face floated above the basket. Somehow, I was going to show him—show all of them—that I belonged.

I wasn't sure how, though. I knew better than anyone how rarely Kansas lost on its home court inside cavernous Allen Fieldhouse, named after legendary coach Forrest Clare "Phog" Allen, whose mentor had been the guy who'd invented the game.

These are two of the ghosts that haunt Allen Fieldhouse. They aren't the only ones.

There's Dean Smith, who'd learned the game at Phog Allen's feet before becoming a coaching legend in his own right.

There's Clyde Lovelette, who'd led Kansas to its first national championship in 1952.

There's Danny Manning, who'd led Kansas to its second national championship in 1988, causing me to go into paroxysms of joy.

I'd once spotted Manning at the end of an aisle in a Lawrence Wal-Mart. We were in town to watch the Christmas Vespers program put on by the university. I was nine years old.

"What should I do?" I asked my mother.

"Go ask him for his autograph."

Mr. Manning, can I have your autograph?

It was still on a corkboard in my childhood bedroom as the game tipped off.

Many years later, Kansas forward Nick Collison would tell me that, at halftime of the game, after I'd outwitted him and his teammate, Drew Gooden, for several offensive rebounds, Roy Williams screamed at both of them, "Do you know where Meridian (sic), Kansas is?! No? Well, if Shirley gets another offensive rebound in the second half, I'm going to tie you to my car and after the game I'm going to drag you there!"

I think I got another offensive rebound in the second half, and I *don't* think Roy Williams tied either Collison or Gooden to his car.

He must have forgotten, caught up in the excitement like everyone inside Allen Fieldhouse.

He could be forgiven the oversight; our game was one of those that made kids like me fall in love with basketball—an old-fashioned barnburner that had all 15,800 fans on their feet for most of the game. The roar they created came at us like waves, so loud that we had to signal each other with our hands.

It was all I could do to keep from thinking about what was happening: we were really doing it—beating Kansas in the place where no one beat Kansas. And I was having a lot to do with it. Coach Eustachy may not have been the sort of gentle soul I wanted him to be, but he was smart enough to take advantage of a 6'9", 230-pound human who was willing to turn himself into a missile in the service of retribution.

At the end, a play went our way, and then a play went their way, and then a play went our way again. And pretty soon, there wasn't much time left, and the game came down to the end of the story, which was also the beginning of the story: me, at the free throw line in Allen Fieldhouse, with a chance to seal a win for my team at Kansas, and a chance to seal something like vindication for myself.

I was sweating, hard, in my red and gold uniform, which seemed gaudily bright when mixed up with Kansas's pristine home whites. Behind me, a giant Jayhawk was painted across the floor. The mythical bird had replaced a massive yellow map of Kansas, the color and shape burned into my memory from those games I used to watch as a child.

I was tired, from all those rebounds and from the days of preparation leading up to the game—the late nights and the post-practice free throw sessions when I'd imagined this very scenario, visualizing Roy Williams's face anytime I got tired or felt like quitting.

The crowd behind the basket swayed from right to left, and I dribbled twice, and I shot my free throw, and the ball bounced once on the front of the rim and once on the back. And then, as with most things in life, it just happened: no more preamble, no more anticipation, no more preparation.

The ball fell through the net.

We'd just won at Kansas.

The crowd inside Allen Fieldhouse didn't roar, because home crowds don't roar for the opposition. They seemed a little pissed off, in fact—robbed of their chance to start the chant that brings forth the ghosts: "Rock, chalk, Jay-hawk."

My teammates skipped toward one another, ready to celebrate, ready to leap into waiting arms.

I walked toward the Iowa State bench, a few yards from Roy Williams.

I'd imagined this moment ever since that visit to his office. Through practices, through early-morning wake-up calls, through summer sessions on the track, through feverish nights with IV antibiotics being dispensed into my arm: Roy Williams's words bouncing through my head like one of those Superballs in the back of a U-Haul.

It wasn't just about him, of course. It was all of them—all those Division I coaches who'd thought I was too skinny, or too short, or from too small a town.

This didn't make me any different from thousands or millions or billions of others before me, driven by something a man said to them.

But in this case, it was me.

And now I had to decide what to do with Roy Williams. The options ran through my head like a menu:

1. Should I shake his hand and say nothing?
2. Should I give him a wink and laugh?
3. Should I flip him the bird?

Then, through the fans, the players, the people from ESPN, his eyes found mine like a Kennedy bullet.

I didn't nod, I didn't wink, I didn't flip him the bird.

I only smiled. And he only looked away. And, because I was 21 years old and because I was fueled more by rage than reason, it was only the greatest feeling I'd ever had.

The Playmate from Missouri taps the side of her empty wine glass with a blood-red fingernail.

"So," she says. "You'd pretty much forgotten about almost becoming a traitor."

I laugh and lean into the vinyl behind me.

"The ignorance of youth."

"You were just trying to square the circle in your head."

I can feel the wrinkle in my brow.

"What do you mean?"

"Well, like people who get divorced. I once read somewhere that usually, when people split up, they're on OK terms. But by the end, there's a good chance they'll hate each other."

"Because of the lawyers and stuff?"

"No, because they need to convince themselves that they made the right decision. Our brains don't like to be uncomfortable."

"So I had to decide I hated Roy Williams, even though, like, 45% of me still wanted to be playing for him?"

"Exactly."

I swirl the few remaining drops of wine around the crimson dot at the bottom of my glass.

"It'll probably only get worse, won't it?"

"What?"

I look up at her.

"The story. As I get older, I'll probably forget more and more about how many ways I could have ended up at Kansas, and it'll become a story about me versus big, bad Roy Williams."

"Yep," she says, rising out of her chair. "It's still a hell of a story, though."

This is what I wanted to hear all along, of course.

We move to her bedroom. She's got one of those memory-foam mattresses, and lying down is a relief after a night of standing around at the Playboy Mansion.

We kiss a little, but nothing *happens*, as it were. It's too late, and she says she's not that kind of girl. And as I go to sleep, I am feeling pretty good about that. Because who knows, it might be kind of interesting to date a former Playmate—take her home to Kansas, have her meet my family. People won't understand, because they never do. But who am I to judge her for being in Playboy? I was in the NBA, and people make all sorts of judgments about that.

Not to mention: she's wiser than she has any right to be.

As I drift off, I'm congratulating myself on the new maxim I've just worked up: just as you shouldn't judge a book by its cover, you shouldn't judge a Playmate by her centerfold.

I wake up to daylight streaming into her bedroom. It must be 10 am. I'm alone, so she's probably in the bathroom, or maybe the kitchen.

I do a quick body scan to gauge how I feel, which is not nearly as bad as I thought, considering that I had way more than one free drink before that bad rapper took the stage at the Mansion.

I look around the room.

Live. Laugh. Love is in blocks on a shelf, and there's a *Dance Like No One's Watching* poster, and such things might turn me off if she sold insurance or taught third grade. But in this case, they serve as ballast, counterweight against the Playboy thing, like all the other things I've done serve as counterweight against the playing-in-the-NBA thing.

I continue my survey of the room, rotating my head counterclockwise, past the dresser, the mirror, another shelf— this one with candles on it.

And that's when I see it.

Above her bed, blown up to 24 inches by 36 inches, is a picture.

It's her own centerfold.

I turn sharply so I can see the whole thing. I'm hoping it will at least be tasteful. Hands covering pubis, that sort of thing.

It is not tasteful. One hand is on her hip, pushing her naked pelvis toward the camera. Her breasts are fully exposed, making the photo more *National Geographic* than not.

But most important: IT'S ABOVE HER BED.

"Hey!" she says from the doorway.

I whirl from the poster.

"Hi!"

My voice has more enthusiasm than I intend because my brain is being overrun with questions.

What happens when her parents come to visit? When friends are over? With unsuspecting gentlemen callers like myself?

She leans into the doorjamb, playing coy.

"Do you want to get breakfast?"

"Uh," I say. "Do you think you could take me to my car?"

Remember what I said about not judging a girl by her centerfold?

That's only true if it isn't hanging over her bed.

LOS ANGELES

A Thursday night

She's sitting in the passenger seat of the four-wheel drive Volkswagen I bought to deal with the Kansas winters. It's a little unnecessary here, where it doesn't even rain but four times a year.

But when I look over at her, I'm not thinking about the Volkswagen or how it's a waste. I'm thinking,

Good GOD, she looks exactly like she should look.

She's kind, too, and that's been the real revelation.

I met her at the launch party for a website that no longer exists and when I first saw her, it went without saying—or even thinking—that I would talk to her. She was so much my type that it was almost unconscious behavior when I walked up to her, stuck out my hand, and asked her name.

I sent her a message the next day and then, for four days, I didn't hear from her, and that might make you wonder: how is that *kind*?

Well, what was kind was that when she did return my message, she explained how she'd lost her phone the very night we'd met. She'd written that she'd liked talking to me.

And then, "This is X, by the way," where X is her name, of course.

Most people in LA wouldn't write that. They'd just assume you would remember.

I'd pretty much given up on meeting anyone special, resigned to an admission that my basketball career had excluded me from relationship normalcy, after all.

And then:

"This is X, by the way."

Until now, we've had a fine enough date. Not great, not terrible, and what I know about dates is that no one remembers not great, not terrible.

Another thing I know about dates is that they're like writing and speaking in front of large groups: if you're not willing to be vulnerable, you haven't got a chance. So I take a deep breath and ask her a question.

"Do you want to hear a story?"

She turns, and I almost gasp.

"Sure," she says.

"It's kind of long," I say. "But it's good. I promise."

"I'll be the judge of that," she says.

I know she will. And I know that telling her such a long story is a risk, because it might mean she's texting her friends tomorrow:

OMG he told this story that just went on and on

But I'm going to tell it anyway, because this story explains who I am now and how I'm different than I was and how I got that way. And I want her to understand those things for the same reason anyone has ever wanted anyone to understand them.

"Alright," I say.

That's it. Just, 'alright.'

She smiles, and that's enough.

13

Rupture

When I signed a ten-day contract with the Chicago Bulls, I had one goal: I wanted to score. The year before, in my first stint as a bona fide member of the National Basketball Association, I'd played five minutes in two games with the Atlanta Hawks. But I hadn't made a single basket, even while being remarkably enthusiastic in my efforts to do so. (In those five minutes, I put up five shots.)

I was more than a little relieved, then, when the nineteen-foot jump shot I cast up a few minutes into my first game as a Bull found the bottom of the north United Center net. Three days before, I'd been in the American Basketball Association, playing for the Kansas City Knights to the tune of $700/week and bus rides from Fresno to Tijuana. Now I was scoring points inside the former home of Michael Jordan.

The only black mark against my shot was the team it came for. You could say the Bulls were pretty awful that season, but saying the Bulls were pretty awful that season would be like saying the Marianas Trench is pretty deep: it doesn't exactly capture the essence of the thing. The Bulls had been ruined by a youth movement that had put its stock in the wrong youths, and the team was tilting and weaving its way through the end of the season like an alcoholic whose habits have finally caught up with him.

It was a level of dysfunction that didn't bother me one whit. I knew the situation was perfect for me; I'd always shined in chaotic basketball environments and knew head coach Scott Skiles was the sort of coach who would probably be impressed by the way I played basketball, which revolved largely around a willingness to throw my body into almost any fray with little regard for the fact that I was almost always physically overmatched in that fray.

Case in point: my new team's last practice before a game against the Indiana Pacers, one week after my first NBA points. Unhappy with the effort put forth by some of the Bulls' youngest (and highest-paid) employees, Skiles ended the day with four straight scrimmages. During each, I moved further and further up the depth chart, aware that, as long as I didn't quit, I would look better than my competition. When the last of the day's scrimmages ended, an assistant coach pulled me aside.

"You're going to play a lot against the Pacers," he said.

It was, as Kate Hudson's character in *Almost Famous* says, "all happening."

Sure enough, I was quick into the proceedings in Indianapolis, checking in soon after one of the youths did something silly in the first quarter. During a subsequent timeout I'd heard the same assistant coach tell Skiles I was "doing a hell of a job on [Ron] Artest," so he might want to "leave me in for a while."

Most of the time, NBA coaches leave their players in games for eight or nine-minute shifts. It's rare even for regular rotation guys to play more than twelve minutes in a row, which explains why I was surprised to discover, the next time I looked up at the scoreboard that hung over the Indiana Pacers' home court, that there were five minutes left in the game.

I'd played the previous nineteen minutes.

I was used to playing in minor league games during which I didn't have to try nearly so hard, so I was exhausted. But I knew that my exhaustion wasn't important. What *was* important was that I finish the game. I didn't have to lead my new team to a win in the process, especially because that would have been impossible, what with us being down by 30 points. All I had to do was get to the end, and this might turn out to be the sort of game that vaulted me into Skiles's regular rotation for good. And who knew what might come from that? The NBA is full of guys who were in the right place at the right time and ended up in "the league" for ten years.

For example, the player I'd noticed on the wing opposite from me: Austin Croshere, who was finishing up a long, exorbitant contract he'd signed with the Pacers after a strangely productive playoff run several years before.

Croshere had caught the ball on a play whose details aren't important and had an unimpeded path to the basket. I knew I could pretend I hadn't noticed him; it wasn't *my* fault he was open, after all. But I also knew that such luxuries are only available to players on five-year contracts. The fate of my career was tied to making the right decision in situations like these.

I dragged my tired but enthusiastic body across the lane, found a position between Croshere's body and the basket, and stuck up my hands, hoping I'd arrived in time to take a charge— one of those fouls you see in basketball wherein the defender falls to the ground and the referee points accusingly at the guy who ran into him.

As Croshere rose toward the basket, his knee slammed into the left side of my body and I hit the floor like a sack of potatoes that's fallen off the back of an Idaho truck, like someone who's taking a charge should. It was a picture-perfect Effort Play, exactly the sort of thing I'd been put on the court to do.

There was one problem: I hadn't gone down only because I wanted to draw a foul on Croshere.

I was hurt.

I ran through the possibilities like a Terminator scanning his hardware.

Wind knocked out?

No, I could breathe. Mostly, anyway.

Did you take that knee in the testicles?

No, that wasn't it. Although it had been a close call.

Ankles? Knees? Concussion?

No. No. And no—I was processing all of this just fine.

While my body continued it analysis, I wriggled toward the baseline, trying to get out of the way so Croshere could shoot his free throw and the game could go on. I wanted Skiles and the coaching staff to remember the job I'd done on Ron Artest, not the time I'd cracked a rib (or whatever this was) at the end of my tour of duty.

The Bulls' head athletic trainer, Ted, was at my side before I'd stopped my weird imitation of an earthworm in a drying puddle.

"What's wrong?" he asked, kneeling next to me under the basket.

"Down that way," I said, waving toward my midsection. My CPU still hadn't come up with a satisfactory explanation.

Ted and his assistant pulled me off the floor and I hobbled to the Pacers' on-site X-ray machine, where it was determined that I hadn't broken any ribs. This was terrible news; my midsection felt like someone had worked it over with a ballpeen hammer and it was only a *bruise*?

By the time I was done in the miniature medical facility inside the Pacers' Conseco Fieldhouse, the game had ended. I rejoined my teammates on the way to the locker room, where I showered, feeling queasy and dizzy. Ted took my blood pressure twice, and I let him, not really asking why; I was concentrating on breathing without making my side hurt too much. When everyone was cleaned up, we got on the bus bound for the airport.

NBA teams use chartered planes so they are free to fly home or to the next city immediately after the game. (And also because chartered planes are really nice and professional basketball players are spoiled.) In this case, we were headed home—back to Chicago, where sweet relief awaited in the form of my room at the Residence Inn across the parking lot from the Bulls' practice facility.

Ted had called ahead and a flight attendant had built for me a makeshift bed in one of the many spaces available on any plane built for 200 but outfitted for 50. On the floor was a thin mattress of the sort one might encounter on a Hide-a-bed, a couple of blankets, and a pillow. I didn't ask why he was being so good to me. Instead, I plopped down and curled into a ball, still concentrating on breathing.

Ted made sure I was comfortable and told me he was going back to his seat for takeoff. He patted my leg, reluctant to leave. Then he gave me one last look and turned for the back. Watching him go was Scottie Pippen, who was sitting in the seat across from my berth.

As a kid, I'd never understood all the fuss over Michael Jordan. The shoes, the posters, the jerseys my friends bought: it didn't make sense. Why would anyone want to cheer for the best player in the world? Wasn't that like cheering for the Sheriff of Nottingham, Gargamel, the big school Hickory High had to play in the state finals? I'd always had a soft spot for Scottie Pippen, however; he seemed stately, noble, and bemused by Jordan's ascent—as if he had a lot to say, but he wasn't necessarily saying it.

After a falling-out with Bulls management around the time Tim Floyd took over as head coach of the Bulls, Pippen had left Chicago, playing the next five seasons for the Houston Rockets and Portland Trailblazers. Pippen had re-signed with the Bulls only one month before I'd arrived. Ostensibly, he was there to play, but in reality he'd come home to retire; he hadn't played a game since I'd been on the team. There had as yet been no "Pippen passes it to Shirley, who scores!" In fact, we probably hadn't said more than three words to one another. This, though, was about three more words than Pippen had said to anyone else.

Across the aisle on our plane bound for Chicago, Pippen looked down his long nose at me like he was a velociraptor and I was a meal not worth chasing. He nodded, and I nodded back, and he returned his attention to the movie he was watching on one of the portable DVD players that were all the rage at the time.

Then the plane began to move.

When I was young, my parents framed the remaining distance in any car ride in terms of the number of episodes of *Sesame Streets* (one hour) or *Mister Roger's Neighborhoods* (30 minutes) it would last. A trip to my paternal grandparents was four *Sesame Streets*. If we were going to my mother's side, it was two *Sesame Streets* and one *Mister Roger's*.

Our flight back to Chicago was supposed to last only one *Sesame Street*. But as the plane picked up speed and the ride got bumpy, it became clear that this was going to be a *Sesame Street* marathon, like they ran during those stupid telethons.

I told myself to breathe, to take it easy, that it would all be over soon. Just like the game, I only had to endure. No heroics, just survival, and then we'd be back in Chicago and I could collapse inside my room.

Liftoff brought relief from the tarmac's bumps, but by the flight's fifteen-minute mark, it felt like someone was stabbing me in the side. Which I realize is a fairly tired simile. I should probably say it felt like someone was extruding my internal organs through a pasta maker or something similarly creative. But the truth is that it felt exactly like someone was stabbing me in the side.

I tried, again, to tell myself to breathe. Like, I said it out loud. But then, after another five minutes of breathing and squinting and hurting and twisting and talking to myself, I turned to my only link with the real world and said, "SCOTTIE! GO GET TED."

Scottie Pippen looked down at me again, his face as placid and noncommittal as it was when he was standing at the free throw line in his glory days as a Bull. Then he unbuckled his seatbelt and unfolded his legs so he could go find help.

As we rose through the air, the pain in my side and back intensified such that it no longer felt only like someone was stabbing me; it felt as if something was growing inside me and wanted out, like I was living out that famous scene from *Alien*.

At the start of the worst of it, I had the presence of mind to wonder how I was ever going to live down the shrieks that were echoing back to me from inside the confined space of the airplane. For a few moments during the game, I'd been a part of the action, just another guy on the team. Now I was making what only could be described as a Scene.

My concern for my image was short-lived. By the time the pilot leveled our plane, I didn't much care about my reputation. Or about anything at all, really. I was just glad I'd found a position that sort of helped: lying catty-corner on the mattress, curled just slightly on my right (good) side, breathing short, rapid breaths.

Since Scottie Pippen had gone to retrieve him, Ted hadn't left my side. As we flew through the Midwestern night sky, I asked him, over and over, what was wrong with me. He said, over and over, that he didn't know. What he did know, I could tell from his eyes, was that he was scared. I asked if there was anything he could do, something I could take for the pain, maybe? But no, he said, he didn't know what was wrong, so it wouldn't be a good idea to start giving me pills.

"OK, so when am I going to pass out?"

Ted grimaced, shook his head, and put out his hand for me to hold onto.

Our descent into Chicago was pure madness, as far as I was concerned. I was screaming and crying and my fingers and toes were numb from hyperventilating, which was alarming to me because at the time I didn't have access to the rational cause and effect of the previous clause. Ted handed me a paper bag and told me to breathe into it. The landing only made things worse, churning my gut like it was a KitchenAid mixer. I might have thought, then, that at least I was close to help, but "help" brought with it another challenge: I was going to have to move.

Midway through our flight, Ted had sent someone to the front of the plane to talk to the pilots. They'd radioed ahead to O'Hare and had gotten permission to land as soon as we arrived in Chicago airspace. An ambulance would be waiting on the runway.

Such are the perks when you're an NBA basketball player. Or possibly dying.

Ted told me all of this, and a part of me—the part we all have that is available to detach from the mind and body and gain something like perspective—thought about how ridiculous this was all going to seem later, if it turned out that I just had a broken rib the Pacers' X-ray machine had missed.

As promised, the ambulance wasn't far away. Three paramedics used the plane's rear entrance and hustled their way to the front. One soon became my gravest enemy; he said I was going to have to help them get me onto the stretcher. Like some ruined wild animal or a drunk Courtney Love, I'd twisted myself into a corner of the berth and any movement meant getting stabbed in the side again. I breathed a few times and then, on someone's count to three, closed my eyes and tossed myself up and toward the waiting medical arms. But I didn't make it; I hadn't heaved hard enough. I collapsed onto the mattress. The paramedic got simultaneously stern and tender. "Come on, buddy, you gotta do this!"

And so I did. My second try was just successful enough to land my shoulders in a pair of waiting arms. Those arms and a few others dragged me onto a stretcher, where I closed my eyes as the pain washed over my midsection. By now, that pain had become almost cleansing. I didn't care about anything—not the future, not the past, not the fact that I was being carried past the entire roster and staff of the Chicago Bulls, a team I'd only joined the week before, on a stretcher accompanied by three EMTs.

When we got to the hospital, three men lifted me onto an examination table. Someone told me that if I couldn't turn over, they were going to have to cut off my shirt. I was fond of that shirt—a blue and white checked long-sleeve I'd had since college. And I had enough neural capacity remaining to think about how wholly bizarre it was, to think that I could be so incapacitated that, yes, sir, you're going to have to cut that motherfucker off.

Not long after, I was rushed down a hallway and into a CT machine. I had to imagine what the route looked like because I had my eyes closed most of the way. My guide was Ted's voice, which was there all along, breathing soothing words into my ear like I was his son.

After the CT scan, I was wheeled back to the exam room where I was finally given a diagnosis.

Ruptured spleen.

Fractured left kidney.

When Croshere's knee had hit me, the two organs had slammed into my backbone, opening up like water balloons hurled at a telephone pole. At that moment, the blood that usually stays conveniently within those two organs had begun pouring into what I learned is called the retroperitoneal cavity. And one's retroperitoneal cavity is not used to dealing with excess blood, especially when exposed to the trauma of a bumpy ride down a runway and the pressure changes of both ascent and descent.

Retroperitoneal cavities are prissy that way.

Thus, the pain I'd been feeling—pain that was probably unlike any pain I will ever feel again, unless I become a very bad bullfighter.

While excess blood in my retroperitoneal cavity was not the optimal arrangement for such blood, my discomfort was not the doctors' main concern. They were worried that I was bleeding from my left renal artery, which connects to the kidney. If the renal artery was damaged, I would need surgery—and fast—to keep from bleeding out. (Or "in," as was actually the case.)

I was wheeled to the Intensive Care Unit while some wizard of radiology scrutinized the results of the CT. Pretty soon, the verdict: my renal artery hadn't been nicked, and I didn't need immediate surgery.

That did not mean, though, that I was ready for a return to the basketball court. Ted told me the doctors were worried about the blood loss, and there was a pretty good chance that they'd have to take out both organs. They'd know more in the morning, he said, so why didn't I just get some sleep?

I was ready to take him up on the offer. Pain makes not only cowards of us all, but also sleepyheads. Pain and Dilaudid, that is.

After I slid into unconsciousness at 3:30 in the morning, Ted called my parents at home. They'd gone that evening with friends to watch our game against the Pacers at a sports bar in Topeka. When I'd gone down, they'd wondered by the way I'd fallen if something serious had happened, and when Ted roused my mother from bed, she said she wasn't surprised to be hearing from him. She was, though, surprised by the tone of Ted's voice, and when she got off the phone, she bought a ticket for a flight to Chicago the next morning.

When your children are homesick at Science Camp, you leave them there. But when your children have just had two of their internal organs splattered, you fly to them immediately.

I spent the next nine days in the hospital—five of those in the "step-down" unit, which is where they put you if you're not quite wrecked enough for intensive care. My mother was by my side for most of it, and a good thing, too. I was so addled by painkillers that I couldn't come up with an answer when, during halfhearted efforts at a crossword she said, "three letter word for man's best friend, starts with a D; ends with a G."

Over the course of my stay, there were many frantic consultations and, as it became clear that I was in less and less danger, many less-frantic ones. When one of our doctors found out that my mother was a nurse (and that I was starting to comprehend words longer than one syllable), he took us on a guided tour of the scan that told my story. The huge pocket of blood had forced my spleen and left kidney into positions like he'd never seen before. I wasn't going to be playing basketball anytime soon.

Or running.

Or lifting weights.

Or staying upright for any amount of time longer than 15 minutes.

I was, though, going to get to keep my spleen and kidney.

And leave the hospital.

The first sensations to hit me were smells. After a week and a half away from the world, my nose had gotten used to sterility. And now, an olfactory onslaught. It was springtime in Chicago, so trees were budding and blooming, shooting pollen into the air. The ground was still wet from winter, so there was peat in the cocktail, too.

I gulped it all in, turning to smile up at my mom, who was pushing the wheelchair I was in.

"What?" she said.

"It smells so good!"

The rest of my senses weren't far behind. I loved the sights and the sounds, too: the sun glinting off the hood of a car, the shuffle of feet as people walked past me.

It was, if you'll pardon the descent into cliché, like being born again.

My mother spent the next two weeks in the room above me at the Residence Inn. The doctor had been right: I couldn't stay upright for more than 15 minutes. Nor could I make it up a flight of stairs. Thanks to all the blood I'd lost, my hemoglobin was hovering around "not enough" and I felt, most of the time, like someone suffering from extreme altitude sickness.

I didn't really care, though.

I hadn't been wrong about the fear I'd noticed in Ted's eyes on the planes. He'd spent several years as a trainer for the San Francisco 49ers and had seen a couple of ruptured spleens in his football days. He knew they could quickly go from bad to really bad and that putting me on the plane hadn't, in retrospect, been a very good idea.

In other words: he'd been afraid I might die.

He wasn't the only one. I wouldn't have been able to express it at the time, but as we'd been flying across the Midwest, I'd known, on some level, that something was terribly wrong with me—that I might be dying. Thanks to the pain, I didn't care if I did.

None of this, though, was something I could express with any coherence. What I did know was that I couldn't figure out why in the hell the team doctor kept telling me I'd be able to play again after three months.

Look, bud, I wanted to say. *For now, let's just enjoy "walking" and "smelling."*

The Bulls season ended with almost no fanfare, and pretty soon I was back in Kansas City. The Bulls had an option on my contract, but again, let's just enjoy walking. And smelling.

I wasn't sure what I was going to do with my newfound outlook. Until Scott Wedman called.

Wedman had been my coach with the Kansas City Knights—the team for which I'd played before being called up by the Bulls. He'd also once been a sharpshooter for the Boston Celtics, and when I told him that I couldn't run or jump, a light went on in his head.

"Meet me at the gym next week," he said.

"But I can't do anything," I said.

"Trust me."

And so I spent the next six weeks of my life revamping the way I shot...and the way I thought about life.

The changes were long overdue. One year before Austin Croshere's knee destroyed some of my internal organs, I'd lost the use of my right arm after mangling the brachial plexus nerve in that arm by slamming my neck into a teammate's chest during a practice in Spain. I'd always been a reasonably good shooter, but since the nerve injury, my form—the way I shot—had become a Rube Goldberg machine, all compensations and tricks to keep anyone from knowing that I barely knew what I was doing anymore.

We started small—me in front of the basket, no more than two feet away, Wedman talking me through the principles of shooting he'd learned as a pro.

As my body healed, we moved further and further away, but my form stayed the same. Wedman's voice was always there, telling me to bend my knees, to shoot using the force generated by my legs, to breathe. By the end of the summer, I almost couldn't miss.

This, though, wasn't entirely because of mechanics. Wedman had me thinking about basketball differently. I got interested in meditation and visualization, reading a book called *The Inner Game of Tennis*, the point of which is to remind us that the cognitive side of our brain is often our enemy, while the instinctive side is usually our friend.

In August after my injury, a doctor told me the pocket of blood that had once been the size of a football had shrunk to something fist-sized—enough progress that I could start running. Then my agent called: the Phoenix Suns had invited me to training camp, my fourth such invite in four years. Once again, I would be fighting for a roster spot on an unguaranteed contract. Once again, the odds would be stacked aggressively against me. But I could tell on my first day in camp that something was different. The first time I caught the ball, on a pass from Steve Nash, I took a shot without a second thought. It splashed through the net. The next time down the court: same result.

I played in Phoenix as well as I'd ever played, rarely missing the long jump shots that made Nash look for me when we ended up on the same team. I survived the first round of cuts. And then the second. And then opening day arrived and, Glory, Glory, Hallelujah, I was still on the Suns' roster—the first time I'd been on an NBA team when the season started.

I'd done it. Sure, it had been a hellish year. A hellish two years, in fact, if you counted that injury to the nerve in my arm. But that misery was all behind me: I'd made my third NBA team. And the best one yet—this was the Phoenix Suns of Amar'e Stoudemire, Shawn Marion, and Nash, who would be named the NBA's most valuable player while leading the Suns to a 62-20 regular season record, tops in the NBA.

Kate Hudson had come back to see me, and this time she was carrying flowers. Nothing could stop me now!

Nothing but general manager Bryan Colangelo, who asked to see me after the regular season's first practice, one day before my debut as a Phoenix Sun. He pulled up a chair across from the one that sat in front of my locker and told me the team had just gotten word that the Memphis Grizzlies were going to "buy out" the contract of Bo Outlaw, who'd been a fan favorite in one of his previous stops…in Phoenix. The Suns were going to have to release me so they could sign Outlaw, whom the Grizzlies were so anxious to have *not* play for their team that they were willing to pay him a couple million dollars.

I was 23 the first time I was cut by an NBA team. I'd gone to training camp with the defending World Champion Los Angeles Lakers of Phil Jackson, Shaquille O'Neal, and Kobe Bryant. At first, I'd been overmatched any time I checked in. But

I made quick progress. I understood the Triangle Offense almost instinctively. I was more athletic than anyone thought. I got along with Shaq. And so, by the third week of training camp, I was starting to dream big: maybe I'd make the team after all!

The call came to my hotel room near the Lakers' training facility (there's always a hotel room near the training facility). The coaches wanted to see me.

When I was finished being released, I went back to the hotel room and fell onto my bed, crying the desperate cries of someone whose world has crashed in around him.

I expected something similar to happen when I was cut by the Suns, so much so that I could feel myself girding against tears as Colangelo's words sunk in.

But those tears didn't come.

Being cut wasn't such a big deal because at least I could walk. And smell.

I shook Colangelo's hand and told him I appreciated the opportunity—but not like an asshole: I really had appreciated the opportunity. Then I wrote a long note to the team on the locker room's dry erase board, telling them I was happy I'd gotten to spend some time with them and that I was sure good things were in store for them. I packed my bags and went back to Kansas City where, after three weeks, my agent called to tell me that a team in Russia wanted me to come play for them.

The Russian team was willing to sign me to a month-to-month contract. If I didn't like Russia, I could leave after a month. The deal would be the same after the second month. Oh and, by the way, they were going to pay me $40,000 for each of these months.

It was my fourth year as a professional basketball player and I'd already made enough money to pay off half the mortgage on my house in Kansas City, which was pretty fantastic, I thought. But one cannot play basketball forever. The nature of tendons and ligaments is that they have finite life spans.

So on Thanksgiving Day, I left for Kazan, Russia.

I arrived at Moscow's Domodedovo airport with vague instructions to look for a man holding a sign with my name on it.

The man was there, and he had a sign, sure enough. But it turned out that "Paul Shirley" was the extent of his English aptitude.

Using a variety of creative hand motions, the man made it clear that we were going to get my bags and take them to his car so he could drive me across Moscow to the *other* airport, where I would connect to Kazan. What he didn't mention was that the car in question had floorboards so rotten that by the time we arrived at Sheremetyevo Airport two hours later, my bags and their contents would be soaked with the melted snow that had worked its way into what was once dry space for luggage and feet.

Inside the other airport, the man handed me the Russian equivalent of $50 and explained with his hands that my flight wasn't until 10 p.m. that night (it was currently 10 a.m.) and that I would have to pay the money to someone for my luggage. I wasn't overjoyed to have a twelve-hour layover in an airport filled with people who looked like they'd been cast-offs from the Cantina Scene. As far as I could tell, there was nothing to keep the angry-looking Kazakhs and Tajiks from walking off with my bags. (Security was not tight.)

But I couldn't hop the next flight to Kansas City, so I waved goodbye to the smelly man and gamely found a spot on a bench, where I laid out on the floor the books I'd brought with me; their pages had taken the brunt of the snow's abuse.

I went to the bathroom twice; each time, I packed everything I owned (almost literally) onto a baggage cart and took it with me. Eating presented a similar challenge, with the added obstacle of the Cyrillic language, which made the word "chicken" look, to my brain, like something Charlie Brown's teacher would say.

After my day of vigilance, I boarded a Siberian Airlines flight to Kazan. No one had a rooster on his lap, but it looked like someone could have if they'd wanted to. Seats were missing, the carpet looked like it had been transplanted from a fraternity house floor, and my seatmate wore the same expression you see on death row inmates who've just been informed that the requests they've put in for their last meals have been summarily ignored.

We landed in Kazan at midnight. This time, I was met by someone a little more cheery: the team's general manager, who apologized for the long day I'd endured and joked about Kazan's location so far from Moscow. Then I was bundled into the back of a windowless van and we set out for the city.

The ride was bumpy and unsettling, and I was terrified the whole time.

This turned out to be not only a pretty good description of the 30-minute trip from the airport to the hotel, but also my next two months in Russia. The temperature rarely rose above freezing. No one smiled. And I couldn't come to terms with the harshness of the Russian language which, whenever it hit my ears, made me think someone was very angry with me.

The next two months felt like six. When they were over, it was time to decide whether I would stay for the remainder of the year. If I said yes, I would be in Kazan until May or June, and everyone said springtime in Kazan was far better than wintertime in Kazan. I would also make $200,000, effectively doubling my career take as a basketball player and giving me some breathing room if I needed to spend another year in the minor leagues, chasing my dream of a long-term contract in the NBA.

But none of that took into account how I felt—about the loneliness, the ups and downs, the bizarre nature of the existence I'd chosen. It wasn't just Russia that had me down. I'd just turned 27 and it had been three years since I'd been in the same place for longer than three months. I hadn't had a girlfriend since college.

I played my last game in the country in a city just outside of Moscow. We stayed in a "resort" that had a bowling alley attached, and I bowled a 112 with the girl who'd shown me the Söyembikä Tower, who'd flown to Moscow to say good-bye. Two days later, the same guy who'd picked me up at Domodedovo took me to the airport. His breath remained reminiscent of a dumpster, but this time my bags stayed dry.

As we arrived at the Departures terminal, he got a call and passed the phone to me. It was the team's general manager.

"How about $55,000 for each month?"

I've never known for sure what my father made as a research analyst working for the Kansas Department of Corrections, but I was always under the impression that it was between $40,000 and $50,000 annually.

I was being offered slightly more than that per month, to play a game.

I looked out at the monolithic airport—no more monolithic than any other, I suppose—and shook my head. Who was I that I was being offered $275,000 to play five months of basketball? More important: who was I that I was going to turn that much money down?

Someone who, quite simply, couldn't do it anymore.

"Thanks," I said with a smile. "But I have to go home."

Two nights after the ten-hour Aeroflot flight that took me from Moscow to New York, I drove from Kansas City to my parents' house at the intersection of those gravel roads I'd grown up on. In theory, I was there to open the Christmas and birthday presents I'd missed while in Russia, but really I was there because I needed someone to take care of me, to tell me that things would be OK, to help me figure out what I was going to do with my life. I'd taken my shots: first with the Bulls, then with the Suns, and then in Russia, of all places. But I didn't have any more shots in me. I couldn't imagine going to play for yet another minor league team, or going back overseas, or wallowing in misery in Kansas City, trying to pretend I was happy with the way my life had turned out.

The funny thing was: I wasn't sure I cared. Maybe it was time to put my engineering degree to use. Maybe, at 27, I'd reached my limit with basketball.

After supper, as I prepared to join my parents in a night of bad reality television while the deep Kansas darkness raged outside, I noticed that my phone was causing a commotion on top of the bookshelf where I'd set it. I considered ignoring it but then figured there wasn't much anyone could do to take me out of the reverie I'd found.

I smiled when I saw that it was my agent. I assumed he was calling to debrief me and to make fun of me for costing him $27,500. (Basketball agents get a healthy 10% of European contracts.)

"I know, I'm an idiot," I said as I answered.

"Who said that?"

"You, I assumed."

"You might be, but luckily, you have the best agent in the world."

"Huh?"

"Are you sitting down?"

"Hold on," I said.

I pulled open the sliding-glass door and flopped into one of the green chairs on the deck that hangs over the driveway where I first learned how to shoot a basketball. I've learned over the years that when people tell you to sit down for a phone call, you should listen.

I rocked back and told my agent I was ready, staring up at all the stars that are available for viewing at my parents' house.

"Tomorrow the Phoenix Suns are trading away three players for Jim Jackson. Then they're going to sign you."

"Um, what?"

"The Suns. They're trading three players away."

"And they want to sign me?"

"Yep. The news will hit tomorrow. You'll fly out the day after."

If my agent had been on the deck with me, he would have seen me shaking my head. I mean, if it hadn't been so dark. Partly at the absurdity of my life, but mostly because, while he didn't know it, I wasn't sure I wanted to agree to the deal. To go to Phoenix on a 10-day contract and try to prove myself again, worrying about every jump shot and what it meant for my future? This didn't really solv-

"Oh, and here's the best part: I got them to sign you to the end of the year. With a team option for next year."

"How's that?"

"You heard me. You're in the NBA again. And this time, you're going to stay for a while."

When my agent was finished convincing me that he wasn't joking, he went over the particulars and then swore me to radio silence with anyone but my parents. When I went back inside, those parents looked up from *The Biggest Loser* with similarly quizzical expressions on their faces.

I looked down at my phone. Then I looked up at them.

"Apparently, the Phoenix Suns are going to sign me…for the rest of the year."

My parents' reaction was emblematic of their response to most of the news I ever gave them about my basketball career. My dad stuck out his bottom lip and nodded. My mom said, "Really?" like I'd just told her I'd gotten an A on a math test.

"Yeah," I said. "I think so."

The trade happened the next day. I flew to Phoenix by way of Memphis the day after that, signing a contract with the Suns for the rest of the season—a season that ended in the Western Conference Finals where the Suns lost to the San Antonio Spurs after shooting guard Joe Johnson broke his face in a freak accident involving the arena floor.

I rarely played on the team's historic run, which would have been disconcerting to the old version of me. But the new me didn't much care. I'd learned some lessons on a plane, in a hospital bed, and on the steppes of Russia. I was happy with what I'd found. Not a spot on an NBA All-Star team. Just a place where, every day, people were happy to see me.

One of those people was an assistant coach who called me into his office one day after practice. He pulled out a digital camera and showed me a picture he'd taken—it was of the note I'd written on the locker room's dry erase board when I'd been cut back in the fall.

"When I saw that, I had a feeling you'd be back," he said.

"Gosh," she says.

I look over. In the window past her, the neon lights of the City of Commerce meld together like a time-lapse photograph.

"Yeah," I say. "It was a long story."

She nods and holds my eyes with hers.

"I wonder what you were like before."

I turn to the dark road ahead, white dashes flickering as we drive across them.

"Me too," I say. Then I glance over at her. "Sorry, that was a little melodramatic. I'm different now. But I'm not *that* different. Like, I'll always be a bit of a worrier, and I'll always have a hard time relaxing. But getting hurt like that—it changed me, made me see things differently."

She nods and I look back at the road.

"It must have been scary," she says.

Usually, when people say this, I shrug and say it wasn't so bad.

"I was so, so scared," I say.

I look over at her. We're passing the Commerce Casino, where I'd once won $300 playing poker and where I'd twice lost $200 playing poker.

"I'm sorry," she says.

And it seems like she means it.

Like I said: kind.

I turn back to the dark highway and tap the steering wheel.

"You know," I say. "I'm not sure I've ever told that story that way before."

"How can you tell a story a different way?"

"Well, sometimes I talk about how the explosion of my kidney and spleen was a good reminder that I'd lost sight of what I cared about in basketball. Which is true, by the way. And sometimes I talk about how, without the injury, I don't think I would have connected with writing like I did. Which is also true. When I was playing for the Suns, that's when I got asked to write for their website, which led to the book deal, which led to me being here in L.A."

"So why'd you tell it to me this way?"

The answer is simple: because, with the right person, it's not about being entertaining or funny or heroic, or telling the story in a simple way so there's a cause and effect that's easy to process: bang, I got hurt; bang, I was different.

With the right person, it's enough to let the story unwind—to let them come to their own conclusions.

I affect a twinkle in my eye and I say, "Because I think you're worth it."

And this is enough, for now.

YOSEMITE NATIONAL PARK

A Thursday afternoon

This one isn't a date. Unless you can call it a date when you go on a camping trip with your girlfriend. We've spent the past two nights in a tent with a broken pole. We've stood over the campfire so long we both smell like survivors of a house fire. We've showered, sort of, in a glorified latrine near the campsite's entrance.

We've done less grimy things, too. We took pictures of ourselves in front of Half Dome. We played with the chipmunks. We took a hike, and left the trail, and the entire time, I marveled at the way she moves, the way she laughs, the way her eyes get big when she's surprised.

Now we're in the same Volkswagen we were in on our first date, driving down from the edge of the canyon that overlooks the Yosemite Valley floor. We're taking turns picking out songs to play on the iPod that's connected to the Volkswagen's radio by way of one of those FM adapters.

She picks out the best song Stereophonics ever recorded: "Dakota" from *Language Sex Violence Other*.

> *Thinking 'bout thinking of you*
> *Summertime think it was June, yeah, think it was June*
> *Laying back, head on the grass,*
> *Chewing gum, having some laughs,*
> *You made me feel like the one,*
> *You made me feel like the one.*

When the song is over, we're halfway into the valley. I tell her to find Bobby McFerrin on the iPod. She looks at me. I can't see it because of her sunglasses, but I'm sure one of the eyebrows I like has dipped in incredulity.

"Trust me," I say.

I drive.

We listen.

I park.

We walk to the main lodge in the Yosemite Valley.

"Will you get a beer with me?" I ask.

She says of course she will. We get in line behind a blond family of four, outfitted in North Face gear that probably cost as much, in aggregate, as a used Corolla. When it is our turn at the counter, we order beers. We take the beers. We sit down. I look around.

And then I start crying. Which is a weird thing to do inside Yosemite National Park, across from your kind and beautiful girlfriend, and in front of a tall, frosty beer.

So, naturally, she asks me what's wrong.

14

Disneyland and Death

To an eleven-year-old boy who's only been on automobile-based vacations to the Ozarks and the Rockies, a plane ride is a wondrous event. One late September day, I was sitting next to Dean Scotland in fifth grade band, listening to him tell stories about the bazooka he claimed his father owned. The next, I was disembarking from my first-ever airplane trip in Los Angeles.

We went to California, in part, to visit family: Uncle Tom in Los Angeles, my father's sisters in Los Gatos, Manhattan Beach, and Riverside.

But we also went to California for reasons I thought more pertinent to my 11-year-old existence. That is to say, fun reasons: Universal Studios, the La Brea Tar Pits, and Disneyland.

I hadn't grown up under the spell of Disney, but that didn't mean I wasn't willing to get excited about Disney*land*. I loved Kansas City's resident amusement park, Worlds of Fun, home to rides with names that were destined to run afoul of political correctness: the Zulu, the Orient Express, and the Zambezi Zinger, the last of which didn't have seat belts but instead relied only on the weight of its occupants to hold those occupants inside.

I assumed that if I loved Worlds of Fun, which was near the boring place where I lived, and there was another amusement park but this amusement park was located in far-off California (which I knew *had* to be better than Kansas), then this far-off amusement park was about to knock my socks off, as my grandmother might have said.

On the day appointed for our trip to Disneyland, I awoke feeling like someone had slipped me an elixir containing the adrenaline associated with the past five Christmases and the two previous Last Days of School.

I bolted for the kitchen at my aunt's Manhattan Beach apartment (we were Cousin Eddy in this portrait), ready to start what I assumed was going to be the best day of my life. I was in for a surprise. My father and my brothers had been vomiting since 4 a.m.

Disneyland was postponed.

Once my mother had gotten everyone Immodiumed and/ or Mylanted and the gastrointestinal coast was reasonably clear, we took our rental Chevrolet Lumina east to the home of one of my dad's other sisters, in one of those Inland Empire cities that looks like it came from the future—a future where everyone has lost the will to live and all the water is gone.

We took an afternoon tour of the small horse farm where this previously unknown aunt of mine lived. The eucalyptus trees made it feel like another planet, and my brother Dan fell in the pool with his clothes on.

After dinner at some suburban restaurant called Claim Snorter or Bootlegger's or Jackstrap Junction, we tucked in for the night, a long day survived. My dad and my brothers had gotten progressively better throughout the day and we were set for Disneyland in the morning.

So it's weird that this was the night I realized my parents were going to die.

Before our trip to California, I'd been dueling with my first-ever existential crisis. It had begun the previous winter when, thanks to a He-Man character named Trapjaw, I'd found out the truth about Santa Claus.

I was almost eleven years old, and doubts about the Santa Claus thing were creeping into my head. The logistics of the chimney's interior diameter were difficult to reconcile, and I was beginning to understand just how many people lived in the United States. At school, none of my classmates spoke to the Santa Claus Conundrum with any real authority. Undoubtedly some of them—

specifically the ones who lived near Nancy Smolinski down by the grain elevator in Meriden—must have been told by their parents that Santa was about as real as their stepfathers' love. They didn't let on, though. Maybe they'd been sworn to secrecy, told not to intervene when the rest of us fought over whether the benefit of an extra hour by going East to West (because, see, then it's still only *ten* here) was enough to make up for the fact that landing on all two hundred and fifty houses in Meriden would alone take up most of that hour.

What I knew FOR SURE was that, in spite of the tendrils of doubt that were climbing my brain's outer walls, I STILL BELIEVED. And just like anyone who knows anything FOR SURE and BELIEVES, I wanted to make sure everyone around me agreed. So, one winter day in the lunch line, with my classmates awaiting their spoonburgers and with me getting my milk ticket ready, I stole a trick from the playbook employed by climate-change deniers and Creationists and I made something up.

At a pause in one of the Santa Debates that had become a fixture in our lives this December, I cocked an eyebrow and to the assembled said, "You guys know what the U.S.S. Flagg is?"

The U.S.S. Flagg was the kingpin, the Holy Grail, the mack-daddy of all G.I. Joe toys—an action-figure-ready aircraft carrier that measured in at a cool seven feet, six inches and was listed at an exorbitant $120 in the JC Penney catalog that was the mainstay of the Shirley family's Christmas wish-making.

Yeah, they all said. Of course we do.

"Well, my parents would never get me the U.S.S. Flagg. But Santa Claus did, last year."

My fellow lunch-liners considered my argument and then, like fence-sitting voters at a rally for Teddy Roosevelt, they looked at one another, shrugged, and nodded. And no doubt why: my logic was airtight. Ken and Jane Shirley would never buy such a monstrosity for the Shirley boys, but Santa Claus might give it to them.

There was one weakness in my argument—a weakness that would have been easy enough to exploit if any of the assembled had been to my house. But none of the assembled had been to my house, so they didn't know the truth, which was that I *hadn't* been given the U.S.S. Flagg the previous year. Largely because my parents are not insane persons willing to surrender an entire room of their house to a toy ship.

But this minor detail seemed unimportant. What mattered was that the levees had held and the anti-Santa tide was still at sea. At home, I went about further bolstering my defenses, dutifully writing out my Christmas list while Matt and Dan argued over whether they should use pen or pencil.

I was very specific. I told Santa I wanted the figurine for Trapjaw, the henchman of He-Man's sworn enemy, the routinely inept Skeletor.

I mailed my letter, the action itself leaving me even more confident than ever. I mean, it wasn't like you could just send letters to *nowhere.* And so, it was without a care in the world that I went with my family the following weekend to the North Topeka K-Mart to finish our Christmas shopping. We split up, each of us tasked with his or her own private gift-giving objectives. I wandered off toward the board games, considering whether it was a good year for Stratego for my brother Dan. Or maybe that would be a combination gift for Dan *and* Matt. Then, rounding a corner, I saw it: my father, pulling that Trapjaw action figure I so desired off the display rack of He-Man toys.

Now, my dad could easily have been looking at Trapjaw because he was wondering why Trapjaw had a detachable wrist that could be replaced with a gun, a hook, or a pincer, or because he was thinking of getting it for one of my brothers, or because he and Santa Claus didn't have a direct fucking line of communication and it was conceivable that the two of them could get me the same thing.

But I knew the jig was up.

My eyes got wide and I ran to the front of the K-Mart, where the coin-operated horse sat next to the poor-people Classified Ads: a corkboard that had pinned to it advertisements for lawn mower repair and babysitting. My mother must have heard me wail, because she came flying up the aisles after me, finding me in full paroxysm at the front of the store.

When she got me calmed down and figured out what was wrong, she said, "Jeez, honey, we didn't even think you still believed. Your brothers, maybe, but I guess we thought you found out a long time ago."

I turned off the salt faucet for long enough to turn and give her a withering stare.

"I guess you thought wrong," I said.

And then I went back to crying.

It doesn't take a psychology degree to figure out what I was really crying about: Santa Claus was a link to a friendly childhood that I sensed was coming to an end. My friends were already becoming less interested in arguing Santa Claus and more interested in chasing girls around the playground with intentions other than that they might be able to drill them with yellow inflatable gym balls. I wasn't at all interested in that latter pastime but knew that pretty soon, I would be (theoretically, at least).

We'd already had the puberty presentation; the girls had been shuttled into Ms. Van Heek's room while we boys had been sequestered with Mrs. Wells. (Fortunately, fourth grade didn't rate a visit from the county nurse.)

"You're going to start noticing some changes," the voice narrating the video intoned. "These are perfectly natural," it went on.

They didn't look natural. Not on that high school kid who watched his little brother play in our PeeWee baseball games— the one who'd wear the tank tops and then lean up against the fence with his arm over his head, as if anyone wanted to see the microphone cover that was growing in his armpits. And it didn't seem like it was going to *feel* natural.

You mean to tell me, I remember thinking, at a high school basketball game while my heroes stood on the lane for a free throw, *that those guys have hair...around their testicles? How are they not thinking about that ALL THE TIME?*

No, I didn't want any part of this growing up thing, this not-believing-in-Santa thing, this adulthood thing. As far as I could tell, none of the older people I knew were any happier than I was. I put this question to my mother, clearing my eyes and asking her what there was to look forward to.

She thought for a moment.

"Driving," she said. "You'll see. You'll really like driving."

I cocked an eyebrow.

"Driving" didn't seem like it was going to be much of a reward for growing up, not least because driving wouldn't be happening for another three or four years.

I spent the evenings of the spring, summer, and early fall moping around the house, acutely aware that things were about to change for little ol' prepubescent me.

I had hope, though; I thought our vacation would improve my mood. And for a while, it did. I didn't have any time to think at Uncle Tom's house, and the journal my fifth grade teacher was making me keep in lieu of homework was occupying my brain during free moments.

But then, in all the excitement for Disney, disaster struck.

As I lay there at my aunt's house in the Inland Empire, trying to force the adrenaline out of my brain so I could sleep, I started thinking about my aunt's husband, who had this weird disorder that caused him to fall asleep without warning. He obviously wasn't doing well, this uncle of mine; I was only 11 and not a doctor, but his malady didn't seem like the sort of thing that just got better. And he was of the same generation as my parents.

Mom and Dad are going to die, aren't they?

This revelation, that my parents weren't immortal, rocked my world. If they were gone, what would I do? What would become of me? Of whom would I ask things like, "Why can't I hang prepositions?"

There didn't seem to be answers to these questions, but that didn't stop me from trying to find them. I worried about my parents' impending deaths. And then I worried about the fact that I was worrying, because if I kept worrying, I wasn't going to be able to sleep! And if I couldn't sleep, I was going to be tired for Disneyland! And if I was tired for Disneyland, I wouldn't feel better about anything!

All of which helped exactly zero, of course.

Then, finally, the portion of my brain devoted to self-maintenance piped up with a tiny piece of advice:

Focus on something small.

Before bed, I'd noticed that my aunt had Frosted Mini-Wheats in her kitchen cupboard. Thanks to the Shirley household's ban on sugar-sweetened cereals, I'd never had Frosted Mini-Wheats. And I had big plans to start out my Disney day with my first bowl.

So, with visions not of Disney but of cereal in my head, I went to sleep.

I awoke to a terrifying sensation: something was happening in my stomach, and that something wasn't going to be conducive to riding roller coasters. Or to eating Frosted Mini-Wheats, for that matter.

I got up and reported to the kitchen for breakfast, hoping I was just hungry. I hugged my parents who had, against all odds, survived the night. Then I poured myself a bowl of Frosted Mini-Wheats—something of a brazen move, considering the unrest within my intestines. Halfway through, I could tell that I'd made a mistake. I sped to the bathroom, where I deposited the few Mini-Wheats I'd eaten directly into the toilet. The bad news, for my dreams of Disney, was that I was the only one who was sick, and we were already a day behind. So we went to the park.

I spent most of the day in bathrooms and on benches while my brothers screamed their way through Thunder Mountain and the Matterhorn.

The good news, for me, was that our vacation wasn't over; there was still time for me to shake free from the doldrums. We'd gotten out of the way our respective bouts with whatever stomach ailment had attempted to derail the trip, and we still had a few days left, including the trip's capstone: Yosemite National Park.

From Semi-Los Angeles we drove up the coast to San Francisco to see more relatives. And then on to Yosemite, where we unpacked our bags in tent-cabins that sat under the shadow of Half Dome. The park was beautiful, picturesque, like nothing I'd ever seen. And our timing couldn't have been better—Yosemite's alpine air was still warm enough that the place was habitable, but the park wasn't overrun with tourists; our parents had pulled us out of school for two weeks for the California Trip.

It was perfect.

Yet, waiting for me like the ninja in the *Pink Panther* movies my parents had rented when we'd first gotten a VCR: that same dreadful, inescapable sense that my life had already seen its best days. It stalked me wherever we went: the Sequoias, Tuolumne Meadows, the base of the sheer rock wall that is El Capitan.

On our last night in the park, after my father relented and allowed us to get pizza in the main camp building, I found myself walking through a pretty Yosemite glade, trying to splinter off from my family so I could fight back the tears that were about to spill onto the pine needles below. The vacation, like my childhood, was ending more quickly than I wanted it to, and I couldn't seem to slow down either one. Worst of all was the sense that, no matter what I did, I couldn't stop thinking about the inexorable march of time: away from childhood, into adulthood, toward my parents' deaths.

And then, over some speakers artfully placed in the woods, I heard whistles, a be-bop, and,

> *Here's a little song I wrote,*
> *You might want to sing it note for note,*

Bobby McFerrin's "Don't Worry, Be Happy," had long since done its two weeks at Number One on the Billboard Hot 100. But I was hearing it for the first time. And, for reasons that I could neither explain nor understand, the tension dropped out of my shoulders, my brain zeroed in on the natural beauty around me, and thanks to something in McFerrin's voice, I did exactly what he ordered: I *didn't* worry; I *did* be happy.

After Yosemite, we went back to Kansas and I re-joined my fifth grade class. I got busy with Cub Scout meetings and 4-H events and a YMCA basketball team, and then my time at Jefferson West Elementary was over and I went off to middle school and those long bus rides where we traded baseball cards and those middle school dances where I stayed scared of Lisa Zerr.

I didn't forget about the despair I'd felt about time's brutality, but I learned how to manage it.

Reading helped.

Music helped, whether it was Bobby McFerrin or Stereophonics or Nine Inch Nails.

Basketball *really* helped. Anytime I felt like I had under those trees in Yosemite, I could go outside to the concrete slab. The ball, the ground, the net: these were things I could count on. These things helped me quit worrying—helped me be, well, maybe not Happy, but at least Not Sad.

Then I began to grow (both "up" and UP).

Freshman year: a mess of hormones and confusion.

Sophomore year: possibly worse.

Junior year got a little better; I was starting on the basketball team AND I was kissing a girl.

Senior year brought more anxiety, but this anxiety was manageable, because this anxiety had a direct cause: where was I going to go to college and how could I survive once I got there?

I decided on a school and I packed all my things in the light blue Chevrolet Corsica my parents had helped me buy, and I drove north to Iowa where, thanks to basketball and an engineering degree, I was as busy as a one-armed paperhanger, as my mother would say.

Then college was over and I left for Los Angeles, and then Greece, and then Atlanta, and then the next nine years, well, they didn't exactly race by, because there was a lot that happened in those nine years. I was busy—busy enough that, without even noticing, I wasn't worrying about death and time and my parents' deaths anymore.

Pretty soon I had other things to worry about: a burgeoning writing career and efforts to reinsert myself into social circles I'd neglected while I was traipsing across the globe. I moved from Kansas City back to Los Angeles, where I got an apartment with my brother Matt, who'd grown up and gone to Colgate, where he'd played basketball himself.

I started a second book, I threw that second book in the trash.

I met a kind girl at a website's launch party.

And then, twenty-four years after that boyhood trip to the Yosemite Valley, with the only career I'd ever really known already in life's rearview, I went back with that girl and we went on a hike at the rim of Yosemite's vast canyon and we laughed at the tourists we thought we weren't and we took pictures in front of Half Dome.

Then we got into the Volkswagen and we drove into the valley and we got that beer and now I am explaining why I am crying in this magnificent place.

I tell my girlfriend that I am crying because I wish I could go back and explain things to the little boy I'd once been: that little boy who found the bright red balloon in the fence surrounding the property owned by his not-yet-dead parents.

Growing up, I would say, is just about as bad as you're thinking it might be. It's chaotic, and mystifying, and downright exhausting a lot of the time, especially if your spleen has just been destroyed or you are alone and living in a foreign country.

And you're right, Little Paul, to be worried, because things are about to get a lot more complicated. Many of those complications will mean that life will be no fun at all because they will require choices that will likely hurt someone's feelings.

Often, those feelings will be your own.

But, in spite of this terrifying picture I am painting for you, Little Paul, you should not abandon all hope. Because there will be moments—moments when you'll take stock and a little grin will slide onto your face. Maybe you'll be in your overheated dorm room at your overfrigid college, sitting at a desk that's too small under a light that's too dim, and you will have just cracked a Calculus problem that you thought was going to keep you stumped for days, weeks, possibly months, and you will drop your pencil and say out loud, "Huh, I figured that out."

Or maybe you'll be in a locker room in Spain and your team full of multinational misfits will have just won a game in a city you'd never heard of before traveling there, and you'll look around, and in spite of the snapped ankle that's going to keep you in ice buckets and physical therapy for the next six months, you'll think, "Wow, I helped do this."

Or maybe you'll be in a German SUV inside a national park where you once thought you'd never again be happy, and you'll look across the front seat at the girl sitting there—a girl you drove, yes, *drove* here after months of dating, subsequent to meeting her at a website's launch party where you walked up to her and told her you'd like to make friends—and you'll think, "Wow, I found her."

On their own, these moments will not serve to make up entirely for the tragedies that will befall you.

Your parents are still going to die.

Your brothers are still going to die.

That girl in the SUV is still going to die.

You are still going to die.

What will help, though, with these frequent reminders of life's crushing relentlessness—what will serve to tether you to sanity, just as you will one day be tethered to a water pipe by a garden hose at a plant nursery—is your capacity to share them.

So, please, Little Paul, pick up that balloon and write a note. And then pick up a great many other balloons and write a great many other notes, because someday, someone is going to find one of those notes. And when that happens, this someone will carry your balloon into her house, and she will set it down on her desk or her couch or her kitchen table, and she will open your note and she will read it and she will close it with a tiny gasp of delight as she puts her hand to her mouth.

She will reach across the table, and take your hand, and tell you that she loves you.

And you will understand that you will be OK.

Acknowledgments

My relationship with this book has felt like a long, tumultuous marriage. Initially, we were thrilled to have found one another—two people who couldn't believe their luck. We got up every day excited by the prospect of seeing each other. I thought of ways to make her smile and she thought of ways to keep me coming back.

Then reality hit, bringing with it the jolts reality always brings. I lost faith in her, and she lost faith in me. We put our commitment to one another on the emotional back burner, each concentrating on other aspects of our lives.

And yet we survived. We made it!

I'd like to say we survived because of the strength of our bond or thanks to the power of my will, but it has a lot more to do with the people listed below—people who were ready with a word of encouragement, a shoulder for crying, or a beer for drinking.

For early reads and confidence boosts, thank you to Dan Shirley, Matt Shirley, Tara Goedjen, Brad Morris, Ewan Currie, Stephanie Carroll, Mark Gretter, Jeremy Goldstein, Chet Wydrzynski, Justin Moore, Todd Gallagher, Jason Trabue, Camille Van Groll, Mike Williams, Dr. Tom Greenwald, Lynne Shook, and Jane Shirley.

For creative inspiration and commiseration, thank you to Kseniya Melnik, Justin Halpern, Phil Hay, Sloane Crosley, Nils Parker, Eliza Coupe, Sarah Neufeld, Ibi Kaslik, Riley Breckenridge, and Richard Villegas, Jr.

For emotional and logistical support, thank you to John and Katie Levisay.

For the tireless work that brought this book to life, thank you to Aricca Vitanza, Chris Schluep, Daniel Bayer (production), Scott Shaffer (design), and Van Ditthavong (photography).

For writerly guidance, both past and present, thank you to Robert Alvarez, Jose Antonio Menor, Jay Mandel, Neal Pollack, Dave Barry, Lewis Grizzard, and Franklin W. Dixon.

For inspiration and motivation, thank you to Phil Hopkins, Katie McElhenney, Amber Christ, Emily Popper, Kerry Kletter, and everyone I've met at *Writers Blok*.

For support and *more* motivation, thank you to Jenny Bahn, Scott Muska, Amanda Oliver, Doug Miller, Paul Merrill, and everyone at *FlipCollective*.

For the pitch-perfect final edit, thank you to Katie Savage.

For providing me with the richest life I could have asked for—the only reason, really, that I have any stories to tell—thank you to Jack Rees, Pat Mahoney, Jeff Lolley, Scott Schuler, Wes Stueve, Joey Eck, Jessica Cordill, Leslie Steele, Drew Rice, Eric Long, Rick Farrant, Dan Hypse, Mark Fox, Sharon Miller, Tim Floyd, Roy Williams, Bob McKillop, Steve Krafcisin, Stevie Johnson, Marcus Fizer, the entire 2000 Michigan State basketball team, Tom Shook, Keith Glass, Christos Marmarinos, Ron Adams, Matt Leinart, Shaquille O'Neal, Peter Cornell, Chris Moss, Javier Mendiburu, MC Hammer, and Dustin from Nebraska.

For letting me tell you those stories, thank you to, well, it would kind of defeat the purpose of never mentioning the dates' names if I mentioned them now.

For patience and coffee, thank you to Bar Nine, Undergrind, and Aharon Coffee—my versions of writers' residences.

For the light bulb moment that saved this book, thank you to Matteson Perry.

And for saying exactly the right thing at exactly the right time, thank you to Stephen Mayer and Katherine Mayer.

We wouldn't have made it without you.

CPSIA information can be obtained
at www.ICGtesting.com
Printed in the USA
FFOW03n1130090717
37588FF